REMEMBER | REMEMBER | REMEMBER | REMEMBER | REMEMBER | | | | ER

BIRTHDAY | BIRTHDAY | BIRTHDAY | BIRTHDAY | BIRTHDAY | BIRTHDAY | BIRTHDAY | BIRTHDAY | BIRTHDAY

BIRTHDAY | BIRTHDAY | BIRTHDAY | BIRTHDAY | BIRTHDAY | BIRTHDAY | BIRTHDAY | BIRTHDAY | BIRTHDAY

BIRTHDAY | BIRTHDAY | BIRTHDAY | BIRTHDAY | BIRTHDAY | BIRTHDAY | BIRTHDAY | BIRTHDAY | BIRTHDAY

BIRTHDAY | BIRTHDAY | BIRTHDAY | BIRTHDAY | BIRTHDAY | BIRTHDAY | BIRTHDAY | BIRTHDAY | BIRTHDAY

BIRTHDAY | BIRTHDAY | BIRTHDAY | BIRTHDAY | BIRTHDAY | BIRTHDAY | BIRTHDAY | CHRISTENING | CHRISTENING

BIRTHDAY | BIRTHDAY | BIRTHDAY | BIRTHDAY | ANNIVERSARY | ANNIVERSARY | ANNIVERSARY | ANNIVERSARY | ANNIVERSARY

WEDDING | WEDDING | WEDDING | HOLIDAY | HOLIDAY | HOLIDAY | HOLIDAY | HOLIDAY | HOLIDAY

HAIRDRESSER | HAIRDRESSER | HAIRDRESSER | HAIRDRESSER | HAIRDRESSER | HAIRDRESSER | HAIRDRESSER | HAIRDRESSER | HAIRDRESSER

DOCTOR | DOCTOR | DOCTOR | DOCTOR | DOCTOR | DOCTOR | DOCTOR | DOCTOR | DOCTOR

DOCTOR | DOCTOR | DOCTOR | DOCTOR | DENTIST | DENTIST | DENTIST | DENTIST | OPTICIAN

BOILER | VET | MOT | TAX | SERVICE | INSURANCE | INSURANCE | INSURANCE | OPTICIAN

DAIRY DIARY 2017

Name	
Address	
Postcode	
☎ Home	
☎ Mobile	
Email	
In case of emergency contact:	
Name	
☎ Tel.	

To contact Eaglemoss, publishers of the Dairy Diary,
ring **01270 270050** or email **enquiries@dairydiary.co.uk**
website: **dairydiary.co.uk**   blog: **dairydiarychat.co.uk**

Year planner 2017

JANUARY	FEBRUARY	MARCH
1 Sun	1 Wed	1 Wed
2 Mon BANK HOLIDAY	2 Thu	2 Thu
3 Tue BANK HOLIDAY SCOTLAND	3 Fri	3 Fri
4 Wed	4 Sat	4 Sat
5 Thu	5 Sun	5 Sun
6 Fri	6 Mon	6 Mon
7 Sat	7 Tue	7 Tue
8 Sun	8 Wed	8 Wed
9 Mon	9 Thu	9 Thu
10 Tue	10 Fri	10 Fri
11 Wed	11 Sat	11 Sat
12 Thu	12 Sun	12 Sun
13 Fri	13 Mon	13 Mon
14 Sat	14 Tue	14 Tue
15 Sun	15 Wed	15 Wed
16 Mon	16 Thu	16 Thu
17 Tue	17 Fri	17 Fri BANK HOLIDAY N IRELAND
18 Wed	18 Sat	18 Sat
19 Thu	19 Sun	19 Sun
20 Fri	20 Mon	20 Mon
21 Sat	21 Tue	21 Tue
22 Sun	22 Wed	22 Wed
23 Mon	23 Thu	23 Thu
24 Tue	24 Fri	24 Fri
25 Wed	25 Sat	25 Sat
26 Thu	26 Sun	26 Sun
27 Fri	27 Mon	27 Mon
28 Sat	28 Tue	28 Tue
29 Sun		29 Wed
30 Mon		30 Thu
31 Tue		31 Fri

APRIL	MAY	JUNE
1 Sat	1 Mon BANK HOLIDAY	1 Thu
2 Sun	2 Tue	2 Fri
3 Mon	3 Wed	3 Sat
4 Tue	4 Thu	4 Sun
5 Wed	5 Fri	5 Mon
6 Thu	6 Sat	6 Tue
7 Fri	7 Sun	7 Wed
8 Sat	8 Mon	8 Thu
9 Sun	9 Tue	9 Fri
10 Mon	10 Wed	10 Sat
11 Tue	11 Thu	11 Sun
12 Wed	12 Fri	12 Mon
13 Thu	13 Sat	13 Tue
14 Fri BANK HOLIDAY	14 Sun	14 Wed
15 Sat	15 Mon	15 Thu
16 Sun	16 Tue	16 Fri
17 Mon BANK HOLIDAY	17 Wed	17 Sat
18 Tue	18 Thu	18 Sun
19 Wed	19 Fri	19 Mon
20 Thu	20 Sat	20 Tue
21 Fri	21 Sun	21 Wed
22 Sat	22 Mon	22 Thu
23 Sun	23 Tue	23 Fri
24 Mon	24 Wed	24 Sat
25 Tue	25 Thu	25 Sun
26 Wed	26 Fri	26 Mon
27 Thu	27 Sat	27 Tue
28 Fri	28 Sun	28 Wed
29 Sat	29 Mon BANK HOLIDAY	29 Thu
30 Sun	30 Tue	30 Fri
	31 Wed	

P.T.O. July–December 2017

Year planner 2017

JULY	AUGUST	SEPTEMBER
1 Sat	1 Tue	1 Fri
2 Sun	2 Wed	2 Sat
3 Mon	3 Thu	3 Sun
4 Tue	4 Fri	4 Mon
5 Wed	5 Sat	5 Tue
6 Thu	6 Sun	6 Wed
7 Fri	7 Mon BANK HOLIDAY SCOTLAND	7 Thu
8 Sat	8 Tue	8 Fri
9 Sun	9 Wed	9 Sat
10 Mon	10 Thu	10 Sun
11 Tue	11 Fri	11 Mon
12 Wed BANK HOLIDAY N IRELAND	12 Sat	12 Tue
13 Thu	13 Sun	13 Wed
14 Fri	14 Mon	14 Thu
15 Sat	15 Tue	15 Fri
16 Sun	16 Wed	16 Sat
17 Mon	17 Thu	17 Sun
18 Tue	18 Fri	18 Mon
19 Wed	19 Sat	19 Tue
20 Thu	20 Sun	20 Wed
21 Fri	21 Mon	21 Thu
22 Sat	22 Tue	22 Fri
23 Sun	23 Wed	23 Sat
24 Mon	24 Thu	24 Sun
25 Tue	25 Fri	25 Mon
26 Wed	26 Sat	26 Tue
27 Thu	27 Sun	27 Wed
28 Fri	28 Mon BANK HOLIDAY	28 Thu
29 Sat	29 Tue	29 Fri
30 Sun	30 Wed	30 Sat
31 Mon	31 Thu	

OCTOBER	NOVEMBER	DECEMBER
1 Sun	1 Wed	1 Fri
2 Mon	2 Thu	2 Sat
3 Tue	3 Fri	3 Sun
4 Wed	4 Sat	4 Mon
5 Thu	5 Sun	5 Tue
6 Fri	6 Mon	6 Wed
7 Sat	7 Tue	7 Thu
8 Sun	8 Wed	8 Fri
9 Mon	9 Thu	9 Sat
10 Tue	10 Fri	10 Sun
11 Wed	11 Sat	11 Mon
12 Thu	12 Sun	12 Tue
13 Fri	13 Mon	13 Wed
14 Sat	14 Tue	14 Thu
15 Sun	15 Wed	15 Fri
16 Mon	16 Thu	16 Sat
17 Tue	17 Fri	17 Sun
18 Wed	18 Sat	18 Mon
19 Thu	19 Sun	19 Tue
20 Fri	20 Mon	20 Wed
21 Sat	21 Tue	21 Thu
22 Sun	22 Wed	22 Fri
23 Mon	23 Thu	23 Sat
24 Tue	24 Fri	24 Sun
25 Wed	25 Sat	25 Mon BANK HOLIDAY
26 Thu	26 Sun	26 Tue BANK HOLIDAY
27 Fri	27 Mon	27 Wed
28 Sat	28 Tue	28 Thu
29 Sun	29 Wed	29 Fri
30 Mon	30 Thu	30 Sat
31 Tue		31 Sun

Dairy Diary CONTENTS

34 EMBROIDERY BISCUITS

Your delicious, home-baked vanilla biscuits will look even more enticing when decorated with pastel-coloured sugarpaste and royal icing. You can achieve delicate, lacy patterns that look as though they have been embroidered, just with the aid of a paintbrush. Add a sugar rose and/or pearls and your biscuits will be the stars of the show!

38 GARDENING FOR COLOUR

A glorious mass of different colours is always a delight in the garden, and so are areas themed by colour. Choose carefully and you can have quiet corners of peace and tranquillity subtly transitioning to bright and cheery beds. Colours affect mood and taking that into account can make a big difference to your enjoyment of the garden. Brush up on your understanding of colour theory and watch the plot of your dreams take shape – it can be just as colourful as you want it to be, right through the year.

44 THE SWINGING SIXTIES

Mini skirts, maxi coats, mini cars, Twiggy, Mary Quant, Biba, tie-dying, beads, long white boots, transistor radios, George Best, mods and rockers, the Beatles, the Rolling Stones, the twist, 'Ready, Steady, Go!', psychedelia, hippies, flower power, the summer of love, pirate radio, CND, lava lamps, Habitat, Wimpy Bars, cheese and pineapple 'hedgehogs', smash, 'Up the Junction', Babycham, lager, James Bond, package holidays, surfing, 'sock it to me', 'outta sight', 'groovy' – fab! Everything changed in the sixties, and there was no going back.

50 ACTIVITY HOLIDAYS

Leisure time spent actually doing something rather than just lazing can be relaxing, surprisingly enough, as well as reinvigorating, not to mention satisfying. Longed to go whale-watching, visit a haunted castle after dark, make your own herbal remedies? Whatever it is you want to do, you can do it. Opportunities to have a go are there for the taking. Whether you want to pursue an existing hobby, learn a new skill or take an adventurous trip, be inspired to fulfil your ambition.

Useful NUMBERS

PERSONAL

Bank

Beautician

Building Society

Citizen's Advice   citizensadvice.org.uk

   for England   03444 111 444

   for Wales   03444 77 20 20

Credit card emergency 1

Credit card emergency 2

Hairdresser

Life insurance policy number

   ☎ contact

   renewal date

Samaritans   116 123 (or local branch)

                 samaritans.org

Solicitor

Work

Other

HEALTH

Blood group

Chemist

Chiropodist

Dentist

Doctor

Hospital

Medical insurance policy number

   ☎ contact

   renewal date

National insurance number

NHS (non-emergency)   111

                    nhs.uk

NHS number

Optician

Other

Other

Other

HOME

Childminder/nursery

Council

Electrician

Electricity provider

Garage

Gas engineer

Gas provider

Home insurance policy number

   ☎ contact

   renewal date

Plumber

Police (non-emergency) 101

                  police.uk

School

TV licence renewal date

Vet

Water provider

Other

Other

Other

Other

Other

Other

Other

TRAVEL

Car insurance policy number

   ☎ contact

   renewal date

Breakdown service

Driving licence number

MOT due date

Road tax renewal date

Service date

Vehicle registration number

Megabus   0900 1600 900 uk.megabus.com

National Express 0871 781 8181 nationalexpress.com

Eurostar   03432 186 186 eurostar.com

National Rail enquiries 0345 748 4950

                  nationalrail.co.uk

Voyages-sncf 0844 848 5848 uk.voyages-sncf.com

Taxi

Passport adviceline   0300 222 0000

                  gov.uk/passport-advice-line

Passport number

   renewal date

EHIC number/renewal date

Travel agent

Travel insurance policy number

   ☎ contact

   renewal date

Family and FRIENDS

Name

Address

☏ Home

   Work

   Mobile

Email

Name

Address

☏ Home

   Work

   Mobile

Email

Name

Address

☏ Home

   Work

   Mobile

Email

Name

Address

☏ Home

   Work

   Mobile

Email

Name

Address

☏ Home

   Work

   Mobile

Email

Name

Address

☏ Home

   Work

   Mobile

Email

Name

Address

📞 Home

Work

Mobile

Email

Name

Address

📞 Home

Work

Mobile

Email

Name

Address

📞 Home

Work

Mobile

Email

Name

Address

📞 Home

Work

Mobile

Email

Name

Address

📞 Home

Work

Mobile

Email

Name

Address

📞 Home

Work

Mobile

Email

Family and FRIENDS

Name	Name
Address	Address
📞 Home	📞 Home
Work	Work
Mobile	Mobile
Email	Email
Name	Name
Address	Address
📞 Home	📞 Home
Work	Work
Mobile	Mobile
Email	Email
Name	Name
Address	Address
📞 Home	📞 Home
Work	Work
Mobile	Mobile
Email	Email

Name

Address

📞 Home

　Work

　Mobile

Email

Name

Address

📞 Home

　Work

　Mobile

Email

Name

Address

📞 Home

　Work

　Mobile

Email

Name

Address

📞 Home

　Work

　Mobile

Email

Name

Address

📞 Home

　Work

　Mobile

Email

Name

Address

📞 Home

　Work

　Mobile

Email

Home BUDGETING

	JANUARY	FEBRUARY	MARCH
Opening balance			
Income			
New balance			
Birthdays/Christmas			
Car insurance			
Car MOT/service/tax			
Childcare			
Clothing/shoes			
Council tax			
Dentist/optician			
Electricity			
Entertainment			
Gas/oil/solid fuel			
Groceries			
Hairdresser			
Holidays			
Home/pet insurance			
Life/medical insurance			
Mobile/phone/internet			
Mortgage/rent			
Newspapers/magazines			
Petrol/fares			
Pets			
Savings			
TV licence/satellite			
Water rates			
Other			
Other			
Total expenditure			
Closing balance			

	APRIL	MAY	JUNE
Opening balance			
Income			
New balance			
Birthdays/Christmas			
Car insurance			
Car MOT/service/tax			
Childcare			
Clothing/shoes			
Council tax			
Dentist/optician			
Electricity			
Entertainment			
Gas/oil/solid fuel			
Groceries			
Hairdresser			
Holidays			
Home/pet insurance			
Life/medical insurance			
Mobile/phone/internet			
Mortgage/rent			
Newspapers/magazines			
Petrol/fares			
Pets			
Savings			
TV licence/satellite			
Water rates			
Other			
Other			
Total expenditure			
Closing balance			

Home BUDGETING

	JULY	AUGUST	SEPTEMBER
Opening balance			
Income			
New balance			
Birthdays/Christmas			
Car insurance			
Car MOT/service/tax			
Childcare			
Clothing/shoes			
Council tax			
Dentist/optician			
Electricity			
Entertainment			
Gas/oil/solid fuel			
Groceries			
Hairdresser			
Holidays			
Home/pet insurance			
Life/medical insurance			
Mobile/phone/internet			
Mortgage/rent			
Newspapers/magazines			
Petrol/fares			
Pets			
Savings			
TV licence/satellite			
Water rates			
Other			
Other			
Total expenditure			
Closing balance			

	OCTOBER	NOVEMBER	DECEMBER
Opening balance			
Income			
New balance			
Birthdays/Christmas			
Car insurance			
Car MOT/service/tax			
Childcare			
Clothing/shoes			
Council tax			
Dentist/optician			
Electricity			
Entertainment			
Gas/oil/solid fuel			
Groceries			
Hairdresser			
Holidays			
Home/pet insurance			
Life/medical insurance			
Mobile/phone/internet			
Mortgage/rent			
Newspapers/magazines			
Petrol/fares			
Pets			
Savings			
TV licence/satellite			
Water rates			
Other			
Other			
Total expenditure			
Closing balance			

Height & weight CHART

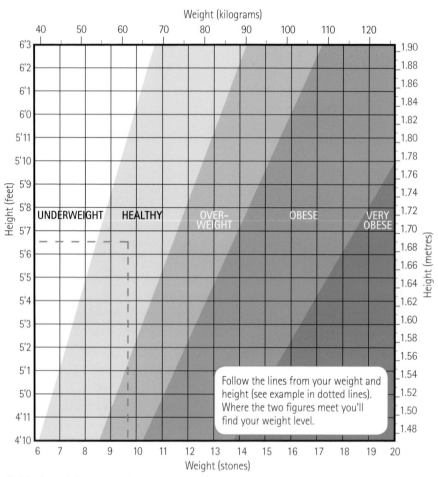

Weight (kilograms)

Height (feet) / **Height (metres)**

UNDERWEIGHT HEALTHY OVER-WEIGHT OBESE VERY OBESE

Follow the lines from your weight and height (see example in dotted lines). Where the two figures meet you'll find your weight level.

Weight (stones)

Guide for adult men and women

☐ You may need to see your doctor if you are very underweight.

■ Desirable range for health.

■ Try to lose weight until you are in the desirable range.

■ To avoid potential health problems, it is important to lose weight.

■ Talk to your doctor or practice nurse. You can be referred to a dietitian.

BODY MASS INDEX

To calculate your BMI, divide your weight in kilograms by your height in metres and then divide the answer by your height again. Alternatively, the NHS has an online BMI calculator (nhs.uk).

Below 18.5	underweight	**18.5–24.9**	healthy
25–29.9	overweight	**30 +**	obese

Metric CONVERSIONS

Length
			To convert	multiply by
1 millimetre (mm)		= 0.0394in	mm to in	0.0394
1 centimetre (cm)	= 10mm	= 0.394in	cm to in	0.394
1 metre (m)	= 100cm	= 1.09yd	m to yd	1.09
1 kilometre (km)	= 1000m	= 0.621 mile	km to mi	0.621
1 inch (in)		= 2.54cm	in to cm	2.54
1 foot (ft)	= 12in	= 30.5cm	ft to cm	30.5
1 yard (yd)	= 3ft	= 0.914m	yd to m	0.914
1 mile (mi)	= 1760yd	= 1.61km	mi to km	1.61

Area
			To convert	multiply by
1 sq millimetre (mm)		= 0.00155sq in	mm^2 to in^2	0.00155
1 sq centimetre (cm)	= 100sq mm	= 0.155sq in	cm^2 to in^2	0.155
1 sq metre (m)	= 10,000sq cm	= 1.20sq yd	m^2 to yd^2	1.20
1 hectare (ha)	= 10,000sq m	= 2.47a	ha to a	2.47
1 sq kilometre (km)	= 100ha	= 0.386sq mile	km^2 to mi^2	0.386
1 sq inch (in)		= 6.45sq cm	in^2 to cm^2	6.45
1 sq foot (ft)	= 144sq in	= 0.0929sq m	ft^2 to m^2	0.0929
1 sq yard (yd)	= 9sq ft	= 0.836sq m	yd^2 to m^2	0.836
1 acre (a)	= 4840sq yd	= 4047sq m	a to m^2	4047
1 sq mile (mi)	= 640a	= 2.59sq km	mi^2 to km^2	2.59

Volume
			To convert	multiply by
1 cu centimetre (cm)	= 1000cu mm	= 0.0611cu in	cm^3 to in^3	0.0611
1 cu decimetre (dm)	= 1000cu cm	= 0.0353cu ft	dm^3 to ft^3	0.0353
1 cu metre (m)	= 1000cu dm	= 1.31cu yd	m^3 to yd^3	1.31
1 cu inch (in)		= 16.4cu cm	in^3 to cm^3	16.4
1 cu foot (ft)	= 1730cu in	= 28.4cu dm	ft^3 to dm^3	28.4
1 cu yard (yd)	= 27cu ft	= 0.765cu m	yd^3 to m^3	0.765

Capacity
			To convert	multiply by
1 millilitre (ml)		= 0.0352fl oz	ml to fl oz	0.0352
1 centilitre (cl)	= 10ml	= 0.352fl oz	cl to fl oz	0.352
1 litre (l)	= 100cl	= 1.76pt	l to pt	1.76
1 fluid ounce (fl oz)		= 28.4ml	fl oz to ml	28.4
1 gill (gi)	= 5fl oz	= 14.2cl	gi to cl	14.2
1 pint (pt)	= 20fl oz	= 0.568l	pt to l	0.568
1 quart (qt)	= 2pt	= 1.14l	qt to l	1.14
1 gallon (gal)	= 4qt	= 4.55l	gal to l	4.55

Weight
			To convert	multiply by
1 gram (g)	= 1000mg	= 0.0353oz	g to oz	0.0353
1 kilogram (kg)	= 1000g	= 2.20lb	kg to lb	2.20
1 tonne (t)	= 1000kg	= 0.984 ton	tonne to ton	0.984
1 ounce (oz)	= 438 grains	= 28.3g	oz to g	28.3
1 pound (lb)	= 16oz	= 0.454kg	lb to kg	0.454
1 stone (st)	= 14lb	= 6.35kg	st to kg	6.35
1 ton (t)	= 160st	= 1.02 tonne	ton to tonne	1.02

2016

JANUARY

Mon		4	11	18	25
Tue		5	12	19	26
Wed		6	13	20	27
Thu		7	14	21	28
Fri	1	8	15	22	29
Sat	2	9	16	23	30
Sun	3	10	17	24	31

FEBRUARY

Mon	1	8	15	22	29
Tue	2	9	16	23	
Wed	3	10	17	24	
Thu	4	11	18	25	
Fri	5	12	19	26	
Sat	6	13	20	27	
Sun	7	14	21	28	

MARCH

Mon		7	14	21	28
Tue	1	8	15	22	29
Wed	2	9	16	23	30
Thu	3	10	17	24	31
Fri	4	11	18	25	
Sat	5	12	19	26	
Sun	6	13	20	27	

APRIL

Mon		4	11	18	25
Tue		5	12	19	26
Wed		6	13	20	27
Thu		7	14	21	28
Fri	1	8	15	22	29
Sat	2	9	16	23	30
Sun	3	10	17	24	

MAY

Mon	2	9	16	23	30
Tue	3	10	17	24	31
Wed	4	11	18	25	
Thu	5	12	19	26	
Fri	6	13	20	27	
Sat	7	14	21	28	
Sun	1	8	15	22	29

JUNE

Mon		6	13	20	27
Tue		7	14	21	28
Wed	1	8	15	22	29
Thu	2	9	16	23	30
Fri	3	10	17	24	
Sat	4	11	18	25	
Sun	5	12	19	26	

JULY

Mon		4	11	18	25
Tue		5	12	19	26
Wed		6	13	20	27
Thu		7	14	21	28
Fri	1	8	15	22	29
Sat	2	9	16	23	30
Sun	3	10	17	24	31

AUGUST

Mon	1	8	15	22	29
Tue	2	9	16	23	30
Wed	3	10	17	24	31
Thu	4	11	18	25	
Fri	5	12	19	26	
Sat	6	13	20	27	
Sun	7	14	21	28	

SEPTEMBER

Mon		5	12	19	26
Tue		6	13	20	27
Wed		7	14	21	28
Thu	1	8	15	22	29
Fri	2	9	16	23	30
Sat	3	10	17	24	
Sun	4	11	18	25	

OCTOBER

Mon	3	10	17	24	31
Tue	4	11	18	25	
Wed	5	12	19	26	
Thu	6	13	20	27	
Fri	7	14	21	28	
Sat	1	8	15	22	29
Sun	2	9	16	23	30

NOVEMBER

Mon		7	14	21	28
Tue	1	8	15	22	29
Wed	2	9	16	23	30
Thu	3	10	17	24	
Fri	4	11	18	25	
Sat	5	12	19	26	
Sun	6	13	20	27	

DECEMBER

Mon		5	12	19	26
Tue		6	13	20	27
Wed		7	14	21	28
Thu	1	8	15	22	29
Fri	2	9	16	23	30
Sat	3	10	17	24	31
Sun	4	11	18	25	

2018

JANUARY

Mon	1	8	15	22	29
Tue	2	9	16	23	30
Wed	3	10	17	24	31
Thu	4	11	18	25	
Fri	5	12	19	26	
Sat	6	13	20	27	
Sun	7	14	21	28	

FEBRUARY

Mon		5	12	19	26
Tue		6	13	20	27
Wed		7	14	21	28
Thu	1	8	15	22	
Fri	2	9	16	23	
Sat	3	10	17	24	
Sun	4	11	18	25	

MARCH

Mon		5	12	19	26
Tue		6	13	20	27
Wed		7	14	21	28
Thu	1	8	15	22	29
Fri	2	9	16	23	30
Sat	3	10	17	24	31
Sun	4	11	18	25	

APRIL

Mon	2	9	16	23	30
Tue	3	10	17	24	
Wed	4	11	18	25	
Thu	5	12	19	26	
Fri	6	13	20	27	
Sat	7	14	21	28	
Sun	1	8	15	22	29

MAY

Mon		7	14	21	28
Tue	1	8	15	22	29
Wed	2	9	16	23	30
Thu	3	10	17	24	31
Fri	4	11	18	25	
Sat	5	12	19	26	
Sun	6	13	20	27	

JUNE

Mon		4	11	18	25
Tue		5	12	19	26
Wed		6	13	20	27
Thu		7	14	21	28
Fri	1	8	15	22	29
Sat	2	9	16	23	30
Sun	3	10	17	24	

JULY

Mon	2	9	16	23	30
Tue	3	10	17	24	31
Wed	4	11	18	25	
Thu	5	12	19	26	
Fri	6	13	20	27	
Sat	7	14	21	28	
Sun	1	8	15	22	29

AUGUST

Mon		6	13	20	27
Tue		7	14	21	28
Wed	1	8	15	22	29
Thu	2	9	16	23	30
Fri	3	10	17	24	31
Sat	4	11	18	25	
Sun	5	12	19	26	

SEPTEMBER

Mon		3	10	17	24
Tue		4	11	18	25
Wed		5	12	19	26
Thu		6	13	20	27
Fri		7	14	21	28
Sat	1	8	15	22	29
Sun	2	9	16	23	30

OCTOBER

Mon	1	8	15	22	29
Tue	2	9	16	23	30
Wed	3	10	17	24	31
Thu	4	11	18	25	
Fri	5	12	19	26	
Sat	6	13	20	27	
Sun	7	14	21	28	

NOVEMBER

Mon		5	12	19	26
Tue		6	13	20	27
Wed		7	14	21	28
Thu	1	8	15	22	29
Fri	2	9	16	23	30
Sat	3	10	17	24	
Sun	4	11	18	25	

DECEMBER

Mon		3	10	17	24	31
Tue		4	11	18	25	
Wed		5	12	19	26	
Thu		6	13	20	27	
Fri		7	14	21	28	
Sat	1	8	15	22	29
Sun	2	9	16	23	30

2017

JANUARY

Mon		2	9	16	23	30
Tue		3	10	17	24	31
Wed		4	11	18	25	
Thu		5	12	19	26	
Fri		6	13	20	27	
Sat		7	14	21	28	
Sun	1	8	15	22	29	

FEBRUARY

Mon			6	13	20	27
Tue			7	14	21	28
Wed		1	8	15	22	
Thu		2	9	16	23	
Fri		3	10	17	24	
Sat		4	11	18	25	
Sun		5	12	19	26	

MARCH

Mon			6	13	20	27
Tue			7	14	21	28
Wed		1	8	15	22	29
Thu		2	9	16	23	30
Fri		3	10	17	24	31
Sat		4	11	18	25	
Sun		5	12	19	26	

APRIL

Mon		3	10	17	24	
Tue		4	11	18	25	
Wed		5	12	19	26	
Thu		6	13	20	27	
Fri		7	14	21	28	
Sat	1	8	15	22	29	
Sun	2	9	16	23	30	

MAY

Mon	1	8	15	22	29
Tue	2	9	16	23	30
Wed	3	10	17	24	31
Thu	4	11	18	25	
Fri	5	12	19	26	
Sat	6	13	20	27	
Sun	7	14	21	28	

JUNE

Mon		5	12	19	26
Tue		6	13	20	27
Wed		7	14	21	28
Thu	1	8	15	22	29
Fri	2	9	16	23	30
Sat	3	10	17	24	
Sun	4	11	18	25	

JULY

Mon		3	10	17	24	31
Tue		4	11	18	25	
Wed		5	12	19	26	
Thu		6	13	20	27	
Fri		7	14	21	28	
Sat	1	8	15	22	29	
Sun	2	9	16	23	30	

AUGUST

Mon		7	14	21	28
Tue	1	8	15	22	29
Wed	2	9	16	23	30
Thu	3	10	17	24	31
Fri	4	11	18	25	
Sat	5	12	19	26	
Sun	6	13	20	27	

SEPTEMBER

Mon		4	11	18	25
Tue		5	12	19	26
Wed		6	13	20	27
Thu		7	14	21	28
Fri	1	8	15	22	29
Sat	2	9	16	23	30
Sun	3	10	17	24	

OCTOBER

Mon		2	9	16	23	30
Tue		3	10	17	24	31
Wed		4	11	18	25	
Thu		5	12	19	26	
Fri		6	13	20	27	
Sat		7	14	21	28	
Sun	1	8	15	22	29	

NOVEMBER

Mon			6	13	20	27
Tue			7	14	21	28
Wed		1	8	15	22	29
Thu		2	9	16	23	30
Fri		3	10	17	24	
Sat		4	11	18	25	
Sun		5	12	19	26	

DECEMBER

Mon		4	11	18	25
Tue		5	12	19	26
Wed		6	13	20	27
Thu		7	14	21	28
Fri	1	8	15	22	29
Sat	2	9	16	23	30
Sun	3	10	17	24	31

Calendar DATES

UK HOLIDAYS†

	2017	2018
New Year	Jan 2*	Jan 1
New Year (Scotland)	Jan 2/3*	Jan 1/2
St Patrick's Day (Northern Ireland)	Mar 17	Mar 19*
Good Friday	Apr 14	Mar 30
Easter Monday (except Scotland)	Apr 17	Apr 2
Early Spring	May 1	May 7
Spring	May 29	May 28
Battle of the Boyne (Northern Ireland)	Jul 12	Jul 12
Summer (Scotland)	Aug 7	Aug 6
Summer (except Scotland)	Aug 28	Aug 27
Christmas Day	Dec 25	Dec 25
Boxing Day	Dec 26	Dec 26

NOTABLE DATES

Burns' Night	Jan 25
Holocaust Memorial Day	Jan 27
Chinese New Year/Year of the Rooster	Jan 28
Accession of Queen Elizabeth II	Feb 6
St Valentine's Day	Feb 14
Shrove Tuesday (Pancake Day)	Feb 28
St David's Day (Wales)	Mar 1
Commonwealth Day	Mar 13
St Patrick's Day (Ireland)	Mar 17
Mothering Sunday	Mar 26
Birthday of Queen Elizabeth II	Apr 21
St George's Day (England)	Apr 23
World Red Cross/Red Crescent Day	May 8
Coronation Day	Jun 2
Queen's Official Birthday (tbc)	Jun 10
Father's Day	Jun 18
Armed Forces' Day	Jun 24
St Swithin's Day	Jul 15
International Day of Peace	Sep 21
United Nations Day	Oct 24
Halloween	Oct 31
Armistice Day	Nov 11
Remembrance Sunday	Nov 12
Birthday of the Prince of Wales	Nov 14
St Andrew's Day (Scotland)	Nov 30

RELIGIOUS DATES

Christian

Epiphany	Jan 6
Ash Wednesday	Mar 1
Palm Sunday	Apr 9
Good Friday	Apr 14
Easter Day	Apr 16
Ascension Day	May 25
Whit Sunday, Pentecost	Jun 4
Trinity Sunday	Jun 11
Corpus Christi	Jun 15
Advent Sunday	Dec 3
Christmas Day	Dec 25

Buddhist

Parinirvana Day	Feb 8
Wesak (Buddha Day)	May 10
Bodhi Day (Buddha's enlightenment)	Dec 8

Hindu

Maha Shivaratri	Feb 25
Holi	Mar 13
Navaratri begins	Sep 21
Diwali begins (also celebrated by Sikhs)	Oct 19

Islamic

Ramadan begins	May 27
Eid Ul-Fitr	Jun 25
Eid Ul-Adha	Sep 1
Al-Hijra (New Year)	Sep 22
Milad un Nabi (Prophet's birthday)	Dec 1

Jewish

Purim begins	Mar 12
Pesach (Passover) begins	Apr 11
Shavuot (Pentecost) begins	May 31
Rosh Hashanah (Jewish New Year)	Sep 21
Yom Kippur (Day of Atonement)	Sep 30
Succoth (Tabernacles) begins	Oct 5
Chanukah begins	Dec 12

Sikh

These dates follow the Nanakshahi calendar

Birthday of Guru Gobind Singh	Jan 5
Vaisakhi	Apr 14
Birthday of Guru Nanak	Apr 15
Martyrdom of Guru Arjan Dev	Jun 16
Martyrdom of Guru Tegh Bahadur	Nov 24

Note: Many religious dates are based on the lunar calendar and, therefore, we cannot guarantee their accuracy.

†Bank Holiday dates can change *Substitute Bank Holidays – New Year's Day falls on a Sunday in 2017; St Patrick's Day falls on a Saturday in 2018.

SUNRISE AND SUNSET TIMES
Note: times vary – these are for London

Day	Rise H:M	Set H:M	Day	Rise H:M	Set H:M	Day	Rise H:M	Set H:M	Day	Rise H:M	Set H:M
January			**February**			**March**			**April**		
07	08:04	16:10	07	07:29	17:01	07	06:32	17:52	07	06:22	19:44
14	08:00	16:20	14	07:16	17:14	14	06:17	18:04	14	06:07	19:56
21	07:53	16:31	21	07:02	17:27	21	06:01	18:16	21	05:52	20:07
28	07:44	16:43	28	06:48	17:39	28	06:45	19:27	28	05:38	20:19
May			**June**			**July**			**August**		
07	05:21	20:34	07	04:45	21:14	07	04:53	21:18	07	05:34	20:38
14	05:10	20:45	14	04:43	21:19	14	05:00	21:12	14	05:45	20:25
21	05:00	20:55	21	04:43	21:22	21	05:09	21:04	21	05:56	20:10
28	04:53	21:04	28	04:46	21:22	28	05:18	20:55	28	06:07	19:55
September			**October**			**November**			**December**		
07	06:23	19:33	07	07:11	18:24	07	07:05	16:23	07	07:52	15:52
14	06:34	19:17	14	07:23	18:09	14	07:17	16:12	14	07:59	15:51
21	06:45	19:01	21	07:35	17:54	21	07:29	16:04	21	08:04	15:54
28	06:56	18:45	28	07:47	17:41	28	07:40	15:57	28	08:06	15:58

PHASES OF THE MOON

● New moon	Day	H:M	) First quarter	Day	H:M
Jan	28	00:07	Jan	5	19:47
Feb	26	14:58	Feb	4	04:19
Mar	28	02:57	Mar	5	11:32
Apr	26	12:16	Apr	3	18:39
May	25	19:44	May	3	02:47
Jun	24	02:31	Jun	1	12:42
Jul	23	09:46	Jul	1	00:51
Aug	21	18:30	Jul	30	15:23
Sep	20	05:30	Aug	29	08:13
Oct	19	19:12	Sep	28	02:54
Nov	18	11:42	Oct	27	22:22
Dec	18	06:30	Nov	26	17:03
			Dec	26	09:20

○ Full moon	Day	H:M	(Last quarter	Day	H:M
Jan	12	11:34			
Feb	11	00:33	Jan	19	22:13
Mar	12	14:54	Feb	18	19:33
Apr	11	06:08	Mar	20	15:58
May	10	21:42	Apr	19	09:57
Jun	9	13:10	May	19	00:33
Jul	9	04:07	Jun	17	11:33
Aug	7	18:11	Jul	16	19:26
Sep	6	07:03	Aug	15	01:15
Oct	5	18:40	Sep	13	06:25
Nov	4	05:23	Oct	12	12:25
Dec	3	15:47	Nov	10	20:36
			Dec	10	07:51

SEASONS

	Month	Day	H:M
Vernal equinox			
Spring begins	Mar	20	10:29
Summer solstice			
Summer begins	June	21	04:24
Autumnal equinox			
Autumn begins	Sep	22	20:02
Winter solstice			
Winter begins	Dec	21	16:28

BRITISH SUMMERTIME

► Clocks go forward
1 hour at 1am on
26 March

◄ Clocks go back
1 hour at 2am on
29 October

Websites

bankholidaydates.co.uk
when-is.com
© Crown copyright and/or database rights.
Reproduced with permission from HMNAO,
UKHO and the Controller of Her Majesty's
Stationery Office

Anniversaries

WEDDINGS

1	Paper	14	Ivory
2	Cotton	15	Crystal
3	Leather	20	China
4	Books	25	Silver
5	Wood	30	Pearl
6	Iron	35	Coral
7	Wool	40	Ruby
8	Bronze	45	Sapphire
9	Copper	50	Gold
10	Tin	55	Emerald
11	Steel	60	Diamond
12	Silk or linen	65	Blue
13	Lace		Sapphire

BIRTHSTONES AND FLOWERS

Month	Birthstone	Flower
January	**Garnet**	Carnation
February	**Amethyst**	Violet
March	**Aquamarine**	Jonquil
April	**Diamond**	Sweet Pea
May	**Emerald**	Lily of the Valley
June	**Pearl**	Rose
July	**Ruby**	Larkspur
August	**Peridot**	Gladiolus
September	**Sapphire**	Aster
October	**Opal**	Calendula
November	**Topaz**	Chrysanthemum
December	**Turquoise**	Narcissus

2017 MILESTONES

500: Luther posted his 95 theses on the door of Wittenburg Castle Church, signifying the start of the Reformation (31 October 1517)

450: Mary, Queen of Scots abdicated in favour of her one-year-old son, later James I of England (24 July 1567)

375: Battle of Edgehill, first battle of English Civil War (23 October 1642)

350: Dutch invasion fleet sails up the Medway (June 1667)

325: Glencoe Massacre (13 February 1692)

275: Opening of Bagnio indoor swimming pool (28 May 1742)

200: Death of Jane Austen (18 July 1817)

200: Elgin Marbles go on show in the British Museum (1817)

175: Regular income tax imposed – 7 old pence in the pound on incomes over £150 (11 May 1842)

150: Thomas Bernardo opened his first shelter for homeless children (October 1867)

150: Last convict ship, the *Hougoumont*, left Portsmouth for Australia (12 October 1867)

125: Birth of J.R.R. Tolkien (3 January1892)

100: Royal family's surname changed to Windsor (17 July 1917)

100: Passchendaele (31 July–10 November 1917)

100: Cambrai – first successful use of tanks in battle (20 November–7 December 1917)

100: Inauguration of OBE (4 June 1917)

75: Birth of Stephen Hawking (8 January 1942)

75: Soap rationing introduced (7 February 1942)

75: First successful use of penicillin to treat a patient (14 March 1942)

75: Birth of Sir Paul McCartney (18 June 1942)

75: Battle of El Alamein (23 October–4 November 1942)

50: Launch of QE2 (20 September 1967)

50: *Torrey Canyon* oil spill (1967)

50: Breathalyser introduced (9 October 1967)

50: Start of Radio I; Light and Third Programmes and Home Service renamed Radios 2, 3 and 4 (30 September 1967)

50: BBC2 first to broadcast in colour (2 December 1967 – after earlier trial at Wimbledon tennis championships)

50: The Beatles release Sergeant Pepper album (1 June 1967)

25: First text message sent (3 December 1992)

25: Windsor Castle damaged by fire (20 November 1992)

25: Britain leaves Exchange Rate Mechanism (16 January 1992)

THE ADVENTURES OF SHERLOCK HOLMES 125 YEARS

Sir Arthur Conan Doyle was reputedly taken by surprise when a series of 12 short stories in *The Strand Magazine* established Sherlock Holmes as a star in the reading public's firmament. Published together as *The Adventures of Sherlock Holmes* in 1892, they were soon followed by a second anthology, *The Memoirs of Sherlock Holmes.* Apparently, Conan Doyle found inspiration in one of his teachers at Edinburgh medical school, Dr Joseph Bell, who impressed with his powers of observation and deduction. But Conan Doyle's writing ambitions lay in more serious work, and so the great detective supposedly met his end, but Holmes just wouldn't be abandoned. Some ten years later, in *The Adventure of the Empty House*, the master of disguise pops up again, causing his old friend Dr Watson to faint clean away. In all, Conan Doyle wrote four Holmes novellas and 56 short stories (collected in five anthologies).

DESERT ISLAND DISCS 75 YEARS

On 29 January 1942, from a bomb-damaged studio in Maida Vale, the distinctive sound of 'The Sleepy Lagoon' fills the airwaves and listeners to the BBC Forces Programme hear Roy Plomley ask comedian and musician Vic Oliver, 'If you were to be cast away alone on a desert island, which eight gramophone records would you choose to have with you?' And so began a national institution. In 1951, after a five-year break, the choice of a luxury was introduced and then a book and nothing much has changed since, except the presenters. After Roy Plomley's death in 1985, Michael Parkinson took over for two years, then Sue Lawley stayed for 18 and Kirsty Young has been in the chair since October 2006. Well over 3,000 castaways from all walks of life have told the listening public about their lives and given away all sorts of secrets they may never have divulged without the influence of their special music and the interviewer's gentle prompting.

COMMONWEALTH WAR GRAVES COMMISSION 100 YEARS

During World War I, Sir Fabian Ware of the British Red Cross was so disturbed by the haphazard nature of burials that he and his unit started to record their locations. In May 1917 the Imperial War Graves Commission was established and after the war, land was set aside for cemeteries and also memorials to the missing. Eminent architects were asked to design them and Rudyard Kipling advised on inscriptions. During the 1920s, over 2,400 cemeteries were built in France and Belgium alone, and rolls of honour commemorating civilians were established after World War II. The organisation became the Commonwealth War Graves Commission in the 1960s. Occasionally, the remains of war dead still come to light. When a mass grave of Australian and British soldiers from the Battle of Fromelles (1916) was discovered in 2009, a new cemetery was made for them. Through it all the work of maintenance is never-ending. Each location is immaculate and visiting is a truly moving experience.

Websites

bbc.co.uk
cwgc.org
greatwar.co.uk
sherlock-holmes.org.uk

Stain REMOVAL

The most important factor in attacking stains is to act swiftly.
The newer the stain, whether greasy or non-greasy, or a combination
of the two, the easier it will be to remove without damage.

First and foremost, check what processes and cleaning agents are suitable for the stained item. For example, wool and silk should not be washed in biological detergent and often need to be treated differently from cotton and synthetics.

Likewise, bear in mind that whites may need to be treated differently from coloureds. In any case, always check for colourfastness before soaking. Chemical treatment may damage old or worn fabric.

PERSONAL

Blood: Soak in cold water with either biological detergent or salt added; or rub in a paste of bicarb and cold water, leave to dry and brush off. Wash in heavy-duty detergent (biological if possible).

Make-up: Work in biological liquid detergent; wash as usual.

SAFETY NOTE

Some of the cleaning agents you will need contain chemicals that are poisonous or flammable, so always read the label carefully and store them away from children. For safety, work in a well-ventilated area.

Perspiration: Sponge with white vinegar, rinse and soak in salt solution or biological detergent. Soften old stains with glycerine. Rinse and wash as usual.

Urine: Rinse in cold water; dab with hydrogen peroxide solution, or soak in biological detergent; rinse and wash as usual.

Vomit: Rinse under running cold water; soak in a sterilising solution, or biological detergent with some disinfectant added; wash as usual.

FOOD AND DRINKS

Chocolate: Rinse in cold water; apply biological liquid detergent and soak overnight if necessary; wash in suitable detergent.

Coffee: Soak in lukewarm water, use a pre-wash treatment and wash in heavy-duty detergent.

Egg: Sponge with cold salty water and wash in heavy-duty detergent (biological if possible).

Gravy: Soak in biological detergent and cold water; wash as usual.

Grease: Cover with bicarb, leave for an hour or so and brush off; soak in liquid detergent, if necessary, and wash in water as hot as the fabric allows. Use biological detergent if possible.

Milk and fruit juice: Rinse in cold water, then soak in liquid detergent and wash in water as hot as the fabric allows. Use biological detergent if possible.

Oil/salad dressings: Blot and dab gently with biological liquid detergent; or sprinkle with bicarb to absorb grease, brush off and soak in washing-up liquid. Wash as normal.

Tea: Soak in lukewarm water, use a pre-wash treatment and wash in heavy-duty detergent; or dab with lemon juice, rinse and wash in biological detergent; or pour white vinegar solution over the stain, leave for 10 minutes and wash as usual.

Tomato sauce: Dab gently with biological liquid detergent and wash as usual; or rinse in cold water, dab with white vinegar, rinse and wash as usual.

Wine: For red wine, pour soda water over the stain, blot, cover with salt and leave for 30 minutes. Soak in cold water; sponge with detergent (biological if possible). For white wine, rinse in warm water and dab with biological liquid detergent

CLEANING KIT

Bicarbonate of soda:
Use this – or cornflour or talcum powder – to absorb grease and oil.

Detergents
Biological/non-biological/ heavy-duty. Don't use biological detergent, or any other enzyme-based cleaner, on wool or silk.

Eucalyptus oil
Available from essential oils section of major chemists. Good for greasy stains.

Hydrogen peroxide
Ask your chemist for 3%, which is 10 volume strength (VS). Don't use on wool or silk.

Methylated spirits
Available from diy stores. Apply with cotton-wool buds. Don't use on fabric containing acetate or triacetate.

Pre-wash treatments
Some of these are formulated to treat a whole raft of common stains, some are more specific. Follow the instructions on the container.

White distilled vinegar
Use as a solution of 15ml vinegar to 300ml water (3 tsp to ½ pint).

White spirit
Available from diy stores. Good for paint and grease.

(white vinegar for silk and wool). Rinse and wash as normal. On upholstery and carpets, cover with salt, leave to absorb and then brush off. Dab with warm water and biological detergent and then with cold water.

MISCELLANEOUS

Grass: Dab with methylated spirits and rinse off with warm soapy water. Use a pre-wash treatment and wash in heavy-duty detergent .

Ink (ballpoint or felt tip):
Dab with methylated spirits; rinse and sponge with biological liquid detergent; wash as usual. If stain persists, treat as rust.

Mildew: Bleach white fabrics, or soak, then wash in heavy-duty detergent (with bleach).

Rust: Dab with lemon juice, cover with salt, leave for an hour; rinse and wash as usual.

Tar: Pour on a little eucalyptus oil, then dab with more eucalyptus oil, using kitchen paper; dampen and rub with washing-up liquid; rinse and wash in biological detergent in water as hot as the fabric allows.

WHAT TO DO

■ Remove any solids with a blunt knife, and blot liquids with white kitchen paper.
■ Apply stain remover to a small, unseen area and wait 5–10 minutes. If the fabric reacts, or if in doubt, seek dry-cleaning advice. Avoid treating delicate or expensive fabrics, or those that require dry-cleaning only.

■ Don't over-soak the fabric with a cleaning agent. To avoid making a ring mark, use a soft, absorbent cloth to apply the cleaning agent and work in a circular motion from the outside inwards. Dab, rather than rub, because rubbing can damage the fabric and it can also spread the stain.

Websites
diynot.com
persil.co.uk
stainexpert.co.uk

Washing SYMBOLS

Unless absolutely necessary, try to wash clothes at 30 degrees, because this uses less energy and is kinder to the environment. It cuts down on bills, too. In any case, avoid washing an item at a higher temperature than recommended by the manufacturer, since this can cause it to shrink or the colour to run, which may affect other items in the load. Every so often, run a higher temperature programme with the machine empty, to clean out greasy residues and kill off any bacteria.

Nearly all fabrics are machine washable these days, and most washing machines handle them with the care they deserve. Sort your clothes and linens by colour and fabric type, and check care labels.

LOADING TIPS

■ Fill your washing machine loosely. Overloading not only adds to the number of creases that will need ironing out, but can damage your clothes and even your machine.

■ Garments with care labels showing different instructions may be mixed, provided that you use the lowest temperature and the gentlest machine action indicated, in order to protect those delicate items.

■ Check pockets, zip up zippers, fasten hooks, undo buttons, turn down cuffs and turn-ups and turn clothes inside out.

⊔ TEXTILE CYCLES

Check both the temperature, given by the figure in the tub, and the machine-action, shown by the bar(s) under it. The temperature may be indicated by dots (six for 95°, four for 60°, two for 40° and one for 30°).

Maximum agitation. Cotton cycle
White cotton or linen articles without special finishes.

Maximum agitation. Cotton cycle
Cotton, linen or viscose articles without special finishes where colours are fast at 60°C.

Maximum agitation. Cotton cycle
Cotton, linen or viscose where colours are fast at 40°C but not at 60°C.

Medium agitation. Synthetic cycle
Acrylics, acetate or triacetate, including mixtures with wool, polyester and wool blends.

Minimum agitation. Wool cycle
Wool, including blankets, wool mixed with other fibres, and silk.

Gentle agitation. Delicates cycle
Silk, acetates and mixed synthetics not colourfast at 40°C.

HAND WASH ONLY
See garment label for further instructions.

DO NOT MACHINE OR HAND WASH

○ DRY-CLEANING

The letter P or F indicates the cleaning fluids that may be used by your professional dry-cleaner.

(P) **May be dry-cleaned**

⊗ **Do not dry-clean**

△ BLEACHING

△ **Bleach may be used**

◣ **Do not bleach**

⚠ **Do not use chlorine bleach**

☐ DRYING SYMBOLS

Check the label to see if your garment can be tumble-dried; the label may advise using a reduced heat setting by putting a single dot within the circle. Two dots indicate a higher heat setting.

○ **May be tumble-dried**

⊗ **Do not tumble-dry**

⊔ **Hang dry**

|||| **Drip dry recommended**

□ **Dry flat**

⟫ IRONING

■ The dots inside the iron indicate the temperature setting. One dot represents the coolest setting and three dots are for the hottest temperature. The table (right) is a guide to the temperature to use for specific types of fabric.

■ You should always use the setting recommended by the manufacturer. For some materials the advice may be that you iron on the wrong side of the fabric only, so check the label.

■ To avoid creases, store your clothes in drawers and wardrobes loosely; don't pack them in.

HOT (3 DOTS) Cotton, linen and viscose fabrics.

WARM (2 DOTS)
Polyester mixtures and wool.

COOL (1 DOT) Acrylic, nylon, acetate, triacetate and polyester.

DO NOT IRON

Information for COOKS

LIQUID CONVERSIONS

Millilitres (ml)	Fluid ounces (fl oz)	US cups
15	½	1 tbsp (level)
30	1	⅛
60	2	¼
90	3	⅜
125	4	½
150	5 (¼ pint)	⅔
175	6	¾
225	8	1
300	10 (½ pint)	1¼
350	12	1½
450	16	2
500	18	2¼
600	20 (1 pint)	2½
900	1½ pints	3¾
1 litre	1¾ pints	1 quart (4 cups)
1.25 litres	2 pints	1¼ quarts
1.5 litres	2½ pints	3 US pints
2 litres	3½ pints	2 quarts

These quantities are not exact, but they have been calculated to give proportionately correct measurements.

DRY WEIGHT CONVERSIONS

Grams (g)	Ounces (oz)
15	½
25	1
50	2
75	3
110	4 (¼lb)
150	5
175	6
200	7
225	8 (½lb)
250	9
275	10
300	11
350	12 (¾lb)
375	13
400	14
425	15
450	16 (1lb)
500	1lb 2oz
680	1½lb
750	1lb 10oz
900	2lb

These quantities are not exact, but they have been calculated to give proportionately correct measurements.

REFERENCE INTAKE (RI)

Energy (calories; kcals)	2,000
Fat (g)	70
of which saturates (g)	20
Carbohydrate (g)	260
of which total sugars (g)	90
Protein (g)	50
Salt (g)	6

These amounts indicate an adult's daily requirements for a healthy, balanced diet.

SPOON MEASURES

1 tablespoon	=	**3 level teaspoons**
1 level tablespoon	=	**15ml**
1 level teaspoon	=	**5ml**

If greater accuracy is not required:

1 rounded teaspoon	=	**2 level teaspoons**
1 heaped teaspoon	=	**3 level teaspoons or 1 level tablespoon**

GRILLING TIMES: FISH

	Minutes each side
Cod (steak)	5–6
Dover sole (fillet)	2–3
Halibut (steak)	5–6
Herring (whole)	4–5
Mackerel (whole)	6–7
Monkfish (steak)	5–6
Plaice (fillet)	2–3
Plaice (whole)	4–6
Salmon (steak)	5–6
Skate	5–6
Tuna (steak)	1–2

Times given for fish weighing approximately 175–225g (6–8oz).

OVEN TEMPERATURES

°C (fan)	°F	Gas	Description
110 (90)	225	¼	cool
120/130 (100/110)	250	½	cool
140 (120)	275	1	very low
150 (130)	300	2	very low
160/170 (140/150)	325	3	low to moderate
180 (160)	350	4	moderate
190 (170)	375	5	moderately hot
200 (180)	400	6	hot
220 (200)	425	7	hot
230 (210)	450	8	hot
240 (220)	475	9	very hot

Guide to recommended equivalent settings, not exact conversions. Always refer to your cooker instruction book.

ROASTING TIMES: MEAT*

Set oven temperature to 180°C/160°fan/Gas 4.

	Cooking time per 450g/1lb	Extra cooking time
Beef		
rare	20 min	20 min
medium	25 min	25 min
well done	30 min	30 min
Lamb		
medium	25 min	25 min
well done	30 min	30 min
Pork		
medium	30 min	30 min
well done	35 min	35 min

Let the cooked meat rest for 5–15 minutes before carving to allow the juices to be reabsorbed and to make carving easier.

STEAMING TIMES: VEG

	Minutes
Asparagus	5–7
Beansprouts	3–4
Beetroot (sliced)	5–7
Broccoli (florets)	5–7
Brussels sprouts	5–7
Cabbage (chopped)	4–6
Carrots (thickly sliced)	5–7
Cauliflower (florets)	5–7
Courgettes (sliced)	3–5
Green beans	5–7
Leeks	5–8
Mangetout peas	3–5
Peas	3–5
Potatoes (cubed)	5–7

Times given are for steaming from when water has started to boil.

ROASTING TIMES: POULTRY*

	Oven temperature per 450g/1lb	Cooking time	Extra cooking time	Resting time
Chicken	200°C/180°fan/Gas 6	20 min	30 min	15 min
Turkey (stuffed weight)				
small (under 6kg/13lb)	200°C/180°fan/Gas 6	12 min	20 min	30 min
large	180°C/160°fan/Gas 4	16 min	–	30 min
Duck	200°C/180°fan/Gas 6 for 45 min then 180°C/160°fan/Gas 4	35 min	–	15 min

* Note that for fan ovens, cooking times are generally reduced by 10 minutes for every hour.

Milk PUDDINGS

A lovely baked rice pudding sprinkled with nutmeg and served with a dollop of jam – what could be more satisfying? Delicious desserts can be rustled up from rice, sago, tapioca or semolina with very little effort, and any leftovers also make a tasty treat.

Mrs Beeton was a fan. Before her, the Romans regarded them as an expensive luxury, and the Tudors and Stuarts tucked in to some flavoursome versions. One way or another, milk puddings have been with us for a very long time. Rice pud probably originated in the middle east and India, and was given to the young, old and anyone with stomach trouble because it was so easily digestible and also nutritious. That idea obviously caught on since it's often thought of in the same way today. However, there's a lot more to milk puddings than that. With a few added ingredients, such as dried fruit and spices, you can conjure up a decidedly un-nursery type dish, using rice, tapioca, sago, semolina, or even just eggs.

Tapioca comes from the root of the cassava plant (pearls are better than flakes for puddings), and is a form of starch, as is sago, which is extracted from the trunk of a particular palm tree. Semolina, on the other hand, which has also been eaten in Europe since Roman times, is derived from durum wheat and is often used in making various pastas and couscous, as well as milk puddings. For anyone with a gluten intolerance, though, don't think of trying semolina. Rice, tapioca and sago are all gluten-free.

RICE PUDDING (OR BARLEY OR TAPIOCA)

Pudding rice (or barley or tapioca) 50g (2oz)
Milk 600ml (1 pint)
Caster sugar 25g (1oz)
Lemon rind 1 strip
Ground nutmeg to sprinkle
Butter 15g (½oz)

1 Wash and drain rice. Put into a 900ml (1½ pint) greased ovenproof dish; stir in milk, sugar and lemon rind. Sprinkle with nutmeg; dot with butter.
2 Bake at 150°C/130°fan/ Gas 2 for 2–2½ hours.

Serves 4   V
Time 2¼–2¾ hours
Calories 166   Fibre 0.8g
Salt 0.2g   Sugar 6.6g
Fat 6.3g of which 4g is saturated

BAKED RICE CUSTARD

Pudding rice 50g (2oz)
Eggs 3, beaten
Sugar 50g (2oz)
Vanilla essence ½ tsp
Milk 600ml (1 pint)
Sultanas 40g (1½oz)
Ground nutmeg to sprinkle

Serves 6   V
Time 1¾–2 hours
Calories 163   **Fibre** 0.5g
Salt 0.2g   **Sugar** 10.2g
Fat 4.6g of which 2g is saturated

1 Cook rice in boiling water for 10 minutes. Drain well.
2 Beat eggs, sugar, vanilla essence and milk together. Stir in sultanas and rice.
3 Pour into an ovenproof dish; sprinkle with nutmeg. Stand in a roasting tin with water to come halfway up sides of dish.
4 Bake at 170°C/150°fan/ Gas 3 for 1½ hours or until just set.

SEMOLINA PUDDING (OR SAGO)

Milk 600ml (1 pint)
Semolina (or sago) 40g (1½oz)
Caster sugar 25g (1oz)
Butter 15g (½oz)

Serves 4   V
Time 20 mins
Calories 156   **Fibre** 0.3g
Salt 0.2g   **Sugar** 6.6g
Fat 5.8g of which 3.6g is saturated

1 Put milk into a saucepan and heat until lukewarm.
2 Sprinkle in semolina. Cook slowly, stirring, until mixture comes to the boil and thickens.
3 Add sugar and butter. Cook very gently for a further 5–7 minutes, stirring often.

Alternatively, turn the pudding into a 600ml (1 pint) greased ovenproof dish as soon as it has come to the boil and thickened. Sprinkle with ground nutmeg and bake at 170°C/150°fan/Gas 3 for 30 minutes.

BAKED EGG CUSTARD

Eggs 3, or 4 yolks
Milk 600ml (1 pint)
Caster sugar 25g (1oz)
Ground nutmeg to sprinkle

1 Beat whole eggs or egg yolks with milk. Strain into a 900ml (1½ pint) greased, ovenproof dish, then stir in caster sugar.
2 Sprinkle with nutmeg. Stand in a roasting tin containing enough water to come halfway up sides of baking dish.
3 Bake at 170°C/150°fan/ Gas 3 for 45 minutes to1 hour or until firm.

Serves 4   V
Time 1¼ hours
Calories 148   **Fibre** 0.3g
Salt 0.3g   **Sugar** 6.6g
Fat 6.8g of which 3g is saturated

Websites

findmeamilkman.net
milk.co.uk

Embroidery BISCUITS

These exquisite biscuits, iced with pastel-coloured sugarpaste and decorated with delicate royal icing 'embroidery', will be the stars of any tea party. They wouldn't look out of place in an upmarket patisserie window and they are surprisingly simple to make.

BISCUITS

1 Using an electric mixer, cream butter and caster sugar together until pale and fluffy. Then gradually beat in eggs followed by vanilla extract.
2 Sift in flour and salt and stir until evenly mixed. Bring mixture together with your hands to make a soft dough, then flatten it into a disc and wrap in cling film. Chill for at least 1 hour until firm.

3 Preheat oven to 180°C/160°fan/Gas 4 and line two baking sheets with baking parchment. Roll out dough on a lightly floured surface to about 5mm (¼in) thick and stamp out rounds using a 6.5cm (2½in) plain cutter, gathering up and re-rolling trimmings to make about 30 biscuits in total. Place onto baking sheets, leaving a little space between each so they have room to spread.

INGREDIENTS

For vanilla biscuits
Unsalted butter 175g (6oz), softened
Caster sugar 200g (7oz)
Eggs 2, at room temperature
Vanilla extract 1 tsp
Plain flour 400g (14oz)
Salt ½ tsp
For royal icing
Icing sugar 250g (9oz)
Egg white 1 large
Lemon juice ¼ tsp
To decorate
Sugarpaste in different pastel colours (about 15g/½oz for each biscuit)
Apricot jam warmed
Sugar pearls and tiny sugarpaste roses optional

4 Bake for 8-10 minutes or until their edges are just turning gold – don't worry if the biscuits are still soft in the middle, they will firm up as they cool. Transfer to a wire rack and allow them to cool completely before decorating.

ROYAL ICING

1 Sieve icing sugar into a bowl, add egg white and whisk, using an electric mixer on a slow speed, for about 5 minutes until icing is standing in stiff peaks. Stir in lemon juice.

2 To prevent a crust from forming, press a sheet of cling film over the surface and cover the bowl with a damp cloth.

COVERING WITH SUGARPASTE

1 Working with one colour at a time, knead paste until smooth; on a non-stick surface using a non-stick rolling pin, roll out to 3mm (less than ¼in) thick.

2 Stamp out rounds of sugarpaste using the same cutter as for the biscuits. Brush a thin layer of jam onto each biscuit and place sugarpaste on top. Gently rub the top and edges to smooth out any marks.

3 Lightly press a large flower cutter into paste to emboss it with the outline. Press a smaller flower cutter in the centre. Set aside for about 1 hour at room temperature to firm up.

BRUSH EMBROIDERY

1 Spoon royal icing into a piping bag fitted with a small round nozzle; then pipe a squiggly line of icing over the imprint of the large flower. Pipe a small section at a time to avoid the icing starting to dry.

2 Using a dampened, fine paintbrush, drag icing towards the centre in short strokes to achieve a feathered effect. Clean paintbrush frequently.

3 Once the larger flower is complete, repeat for the inner section. Set aside for at least 2 hours to allow the icing to dry. Then, with a dab of royal icing, attach a small sugarpaste rose in the centre. Use a dry brush to remove any icing that oozes out from under the rose.

EXTRA GLAMOUR

1 As well as roses, add sugar pearls for a more elaborate design; or use sugar pearls on their own if you like.

2 If sugarpaste doesn't entirely cover a biscuit, ice a border.

EXPERT TIPS

* If biscuit dough is difficult to roll out, roll it between two sheets of cling film or baking parchment.

* Unless the dough is really sticky, it's best not to knead in more flour as this will make it dry and your baked biscuits will be tough and chewy rather than crisp.

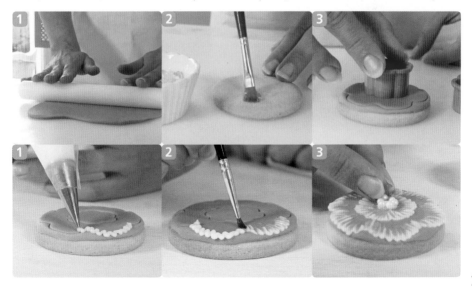

Mini French ECLAIRS

These mini éclairs, filled with vanilla-scented crème pâtissière, dipped in pastel-tinted fondant icing and decorated with elegant bows, tiny flowers and sprinkles, not only look the part but taste fantastic, too.

CHOUX PASTRY

1 Put butter, 4 tbsp cold water, milk, oil, salt and sugar in a saucepan. Place over a medium heat and stir until butter melts.
2 Bring mixture to a fast boil, remove from the heat and add flour. Beat vigorously with a wooden spoon until mixture comes together in a ball.
3 Lower the heat, return pan to the hob and stir for 2 minutes until mixture is smooth and glossy. Cool for 5 minutes.
4 Gradually add eggs, beating well after each addition.

5 Cover with cling film, leave to cool, then chill for 1 hour.

CRÈME PÂTISSIÈRE

1 Whisk together egg yolks and sugar. Mix in cornflour.
2 Heat milk and vanilla in a pan until just coming to the boil. Remove from heat and pour onto egg mixture, whisking constantly until combined.
3 Pour back into saucepan and whisk continuously until boiling and mixture is glossy and thick.
4 Cool, then chill until needed.

INGREDIENTS

For choux pastry
Unsalted butter 50g (2oz)
Whole milk 4 tbsp
Vegetable oil 1 tsp
Salt ¼ tsp
Caster sugar 1 tsp
Plain flour 100g (3½oz)
Eggs 3 medium, lightly beaten
For crème pâtissière
Egg yolks 4
Caster sugar 100g (3½oz)
Cornflour 50g (2oz)
Whole milk 600ml (1 pint)
Vanilla extract 1 tsp
To decorate
White sugarpaste 300g (11oz)
Paste or liquid food colourings
Sugar sprinkles and pearls

PREPARING ÉCLAIRS

1 Preheat oven to 180°C/160°fan/Gas 4.

2 Spoon half the pastry into a piping bag fitted with a large star nozzle and pipe it onto an éclair or baking tray. Spray with vegetable oil to prevent the tops cracking during baking.

3 Bake for 35 minutes until éclairs are puffed and golden. Transfer to a wire rack to cool.

4 Whisk crème pâtissière until smooth and then spoon it into a piping bag with filler nozzle.

5 Pierce base of an éclair at each end with tip of the nozzle, and carefully pipe in crème pâtissière, some in each end.

DECORATING

To dip and decorate:

1 Pour liquid icing (see box) into a shallow dish, wider than the length of an éclair. Dip top of each into icing, so the top is evenly coated.

FINISHING TOUCHES

■ Liquid icing

Cut white sugarpaste into small pieces and place in a heatproof bowl with 2 tbsp cold water. Stand bowl over a pan of simmering water, not touching, and stir frequently until sugarpaste has melted. Add your chosen colouring, stirring, until evenly tinted.

■ Sugar glaze

A sugar glaze brushed over éclairs makes them glisten and shine. Dissolve 25g (1oz) caster sugar in 50ml (2fl oz) water in a small pan. Bring to the boil, without further stirring, and boil for 1 minute. Remove the pan from the heat and leave syrup to cool.

■ Paper bows

Cut 3 thin strips of edible wafer paper – one 5cm (2in) long for the loops, one 2.5cm (1in) for the band and one 4cm (1½in) for the tails. Cut a 'v' at each end of the tails strip. Lightly dampen top side of the loops strip. Bend ends to the centre and press down. Lay on tails strip. Dampen band and wrap around the centre of both strips. Dampen underside of bow and secure in place.

■ Flowers

Roll out sugarpaste thinly and stamp out flowers using a small daisy cutter. Add a sugar pearl to the centre of each, fixing in place with liquid icing.

2 With your finger remove any excess icing from sides of the éclair then stand on wire rack.

3 Spread sugar sprinkles on a small plate and then dip in the end of an iced éclair before the icing sets.

To make striped icing:

1 Knead a little food colouring into a small piece of white sugarpaste. Roll out very thinly

and, using a pizza cutter, cut 5 narrow strips, slightly longer than the width of an éclair.

2 Roll out white sugarpaste slightly longer and wider than an éclair. Lay the coloured strips on top, evenly spaced, and roll over them to fix in place.

3 Trim to size, brush underside with sugar glaze (see box) and press in place. Brush with glaze.

Gardening for COLOUR

The garden is a naturally colourful place – green grass, brown earth, painted fences and sheds. But it's the plants and foliage that provide that added zing, and with a little creative planning and judicious planting, they can provide it all year round.

I n poet Thomas Edward Brown's estimation, 'a garden is a lovesome thing' and so it is, and it can be an even lovelier place if you think about what colours you want to see at different times of year. Haphazard planting has a lot going for it because it's easy and can result in the garden looking beautifully chaotic for part of the year, although it can look a bit dull for the rest of the time. However, much of the pleasure in having a garden lies in deciding how you want it to look, and then watching your masterplan come to life. No need to stick rigidly to the rules of colour theory; taking note of the general ideas can be enough, and experimenting is part of the fun. It's your garden, after all. You can have a glorious mass of different colours if you like – and, in nature, they never seem to clash – but knowing how to use colour effectively throughout the year can make a big difference.

Whether you want your patch to be bright and cheery or a

haven of peace and tranquillity will influence your colour choices. The hot colours – red, orange, yellow – are exciting, stimulating and demand attention; the cool colours – green, blue, purple – are restful, calming and recede into the background. If various sections of the garden are to have different purposes, or moods, the transitions between them are important, too, requiring subtler shades and whites.

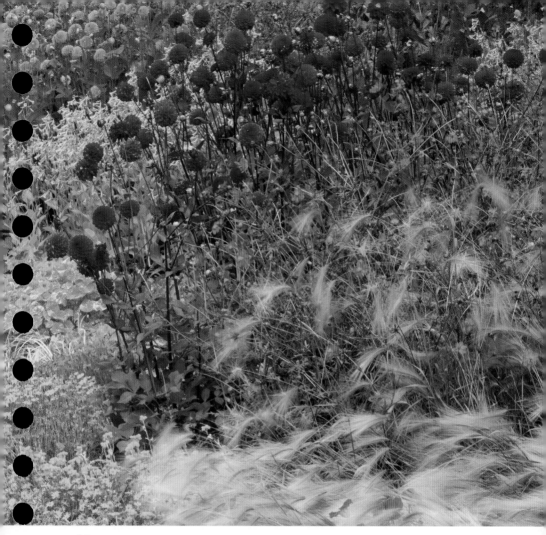

" *You can have a glorious mass of different colours.* "

KEY EFFECTS

The colour value of the plants you are intending to grow is important, too, i.e. how bright, pale or dark the flowers and foliage are likely to be, bearing in mind this is likely to change during the year.

▧ A small area of light colour in a sea of much darker vegetation creates a powerful effect.

▧ Repetition is an old trick that helps to avoid the garden looking too much of a riot. If you love red, for example, have more than one area of it.

▧ Pale colours reflect light and brighten up a shady corner.

▧ Bright colours can look wonderful and vibrant in full sun, while pastel colours will look washed out.

▧ Cool and pale colours bring a sense of depth; bright colours appear to be closer. Planted at the end of a border, pale colours make it look longer while bright colours foreshorten it.

▧ Silvery grey foliage lightens the area and cools down any nearby hot colours.

GROWING PLANS

When choosing your plants, first and foremost, select those suited to the location and soil type of your garden, and plan to position them in the ideal spot for their individual requirements of light and shade. Otherwise, think about containers, not too big so you have the option of moving them.

If you are experimenting with colours, it may be that you will want to move some plants to try other combinations; but shrubs, once established, are mostly better not moved, so be sure to plant them where you want them to be. Shrubs and perennials are lower maintenance than annuals, and since perennials benefit from being divided every few years,

they could be a good bet, augmented by bulbs and, in summer, by annuals. These are often flamboyantly colourful. Remember to deadhead to prolong flowering. Some perennials give very good value,

such as *Phlomis russeliana*, which flowers from late spring to early autumn and has attractive seedheads in winter, dianthus with its pink flowers and silver-grey foliage, and penstemon, which flowers to first frosts.

" Harmonious colour schemes can be elegant and serene. "

COLOUR SCHEMES

The colour wheel, a circle divided into six or twelve, shows how colours relate to each other and gives clues to the effects of juxtaposing them. For gardeners, the six-point colour wheel, made up of primary (red, yellow, blue) and secondary (orange, green, purple) colours, is a useful guide. It may be a good idea to make one as a reference (look it up online), and bear in mind the enormous variety of shades, tones and tints that exist in gardening and in nature, so the colours can be liberally interpreted.
Complementary Also called opposing, these are colours that fall directly opposite each other on the colour wheel: red and green, yellow and purple, blue and orange. Positioned next to each other, they seem especially vibrant, so complementary colour schemes can be eye-catching and lively. A small area of hot complementaries balances a larger area of cool ones.
Contrasting Colours equally spaced around the colour wheel are thought of as

contrasting: orange, green, purple. They tend to go well grouped together – vibrant colours and green foliage.
Harmonising Analogous, or harmonising, colours are those that lie next to each other on the colour wheel, e.g. red and purple, yellow and orange, blue and green. Harmonious colour schemes

can be elegant and serene, or, with hot colours, invigorating.
Monochromatic Using just one colour can be very effective, but challenging. Some contrast is necessary or the result can seem somewhat bland, so use all the shades, tones and tints at your disposal, and plenty of interesting foliage.

Also, when planning a colourful border or bed, remember to choose plants that will flower at the same time in order to achieve the desired effect. As well as colour and flowering season, think about height and contrasts in shape. Tall, upright plants, such as irises, daylilies and foxgloves, mix well with those that have wide flowerheads, such as sedum and yarrow, and spherical flowerheads, such as alliums.

Foliage is an integral part of any garden display, whether used as background or as a focus in its own right. Shrubs such as cotinus and *Fatsia japonica* have eye-catchingly colourful foliage. Others, including berberis, viburnum and holly, have red or orange berries in autumn and flowers in spring.

Among all the possibilities, don't forget roses. A fragrant shrub, climber or floribunda that blooms continuously throughout the summer can do wonders for your garden.

YEAR-ROUND COLOUR

Spring brings sunny yellows and greens, fresh pinks and blues and white morphing into the vivid mix of summer and the warm burnt oranges and deep reds of autumn. Come winter, if you think of the garden as being a colour-free zone, think again. Flowers, berries and dramatic foliage can lift it from the gloom.

SPRING

Shrubs: azaleas, California lilac, euphorbia, forsythia
Perennials: aubrieta, elephant's ears, forget-me-nots, polyanthus

Bulbs: crocuses, daffodils, grape hyacinths, tulips, anemones

SUMMER

Shrubs: rock roses, fuchsia, potentilla, mock orange, buddleia
Perennials: delphiniums, peonies, crocosmias, geraniums
Bulbs: alliums, irises, lilies, gladioli, begonias
Annuals: Busy Lizzies, lobelias, heliotropes, cornflowers, poppies, marigolds, tobacco plants

AUTUMN

Shrubs: spindle tree, rhus, plumbago, Japanese maple
Perennials: chrysanthemums, asters, Chinese lanterns, ligularia,

Michaelmas daisies
Bulbs: colchicums, nerines

WINTER

Shrubs: winter jasmine, mahonia, dogwood, daphne, skimmia, winter heath, clematis
Perennials: winter pansies, violas, hellebores, hepatica
Bulbs: snowdrops, aconites, cyclamen (grows from tubers)

Positive THINKING

Some people are naturally optimistic, others are the opposite and the rest of us fall somewhere in between. Wherever we land on the optimism scale, most of us have days when we need cheering up. That's when positive thinking comes into its own.

When it comes to health and wellbeing, the general consensus of medical opinion is clear – thinking positively can make all the difference. The NHS suggests that 'good mental wellbeing is important for our physical health'. Equally, leading as active a life as possible contributes to mental wellbeing. According to the Mayo Clinic in America, positive thinking may increase life span and even give greater resistance to the common cold – so it's got to be worth a try! In any case, the world can seem a much better place if we feel good about ourselves.

We live mostly in our heads, and thoughts constantly flit through our minds unbidden. The first step in cultivating positive thinking is consciously to challenge any automatic negativity. That means not always imagining the worst is going to happen and trying not to be too self-critical. Positive thinking doesn't mean ignoring problems; rather it can help you deal with them more effectively and with minimal stress. Look for the positive spin.

Time spent with friends and family encourages a positive outlook, and performing acts of kindness for others, however small, can do the same. Help a mother down the stairs with a buggy, hold a door open, cut the grass for an elderly neighbour, or even volunteer at your local community centre if you have the time.

MINDFULNESS

Another step towards positive thinking is to take the time to appreciate life in general, and your own life in particular.

" *Good mental wellbeing is important for our physical health.* "

Remember to stop and smell the roses – that may be a well-worn notion but it works, and pretty much sums up what is usually meant by mindfulness. Some people call it living in the moment, becoming aware of everything around you – sights, smells, sounds, tastes, your feelings, yourself. Focus on things as they are at that moment, accept them without judgement, and you will start to see things you have taken for granted in a new light.

That, of course, may be easier said than done. It's sometimes hard enough to find a moment to sit down with a cup of tea, and even then we're usually thinking about the what, where and when of day-to-day life. However, a couple of tried and tested techniques can help (see box),

TECHNIQUES TO TRY

■ Concentrate on your breathing for a few minutes, using the nose only. Breathe in slowly, hold for a count of six, breathe out slowly. Feel the sensation of breathing. Notice any thoughts that come into your mind and let them wander out again, returning your attention to your breath. This is very calming, and a step towards meditation, which is often advocated for helping to relieve stress and as an aid to positive thinking.

■ Study a flower or an insect intensely, or watch clouds. Listen to music, birdsong or the sea. Allow yourself to become fully absorbed so that you lose track of time.

if you can find a few minutes in the day to practise them.

If you put your mind to it, positive thinking can become a habit, and its multitude of health benefits mean it's a good one to acquire.

Websites
....
mayoclinic.org/healthy-lifestyle
mindfulnet.org
nhs.uk

The swinging SIXTIES

Who remembers the sixties? They say if you do, you weren't there, but that's not true. Not everyone was partying their lives away. You didn't have to embrace the lifestyle in order to wear the clothes, listen to the music and drive the cars.

In the sixties, everything changed. Children and teenagers no longer looked like a younger version of their parents. Mini skirts and maxi coats took the fashion world by storm. Twiggy, with her big, mascara-ed eyes and short hair, was as different from previous models as could be imagined, in her Mary Quant clothes. Biba's – softly lit, full of beads, feathers and velvet, all mauves, purples and maroons – was laid out more like a museum than a shop, and Carnaby Street was the place to be seen.

Young men grew their hair below their shoulders or had a mop top, like the Beatles. Records were made of vinyl and being in the top ten meant selling thousands of singles (45 rpm). Any number of Liverpool groups made it and then came the Rolling Stones. Mums and dads tended to like the Beatles, because they were neat and tidy, but disapproved of the Stones, because they were not.

END OF AN ERA

Despite all this, for the most part, everyday life carried on much as normal, but it was only a matter of time before that was to change, too. The baker still delivered to the door, the coalman brought the fuel – no central heating – and the chimney sweep came every year, leaving a thin layer of soot in his wake. Shopping had to be done every few days because not everyone had a fridge and no one had a freezer; and going shopping took a while – you had to queue up at the counter and ask for every item.

"In the sixties, everything changed."

Food was basically variations on meat and two veg. Spaghetti came in tins in tomato sauce and rice was for pudding. Vegetarians were considered weird. Chinese and Indian restaurants were proliferating, though, so much so that Vesta brought out a ready-made curry and chow mein. Other staples were Bird's Eye fish fingers, Fray Bentos pies in tins and Cadbury's Smash, not to mention fishpaste sandwiches, and afterwards Angel Delight.

Families sat round the table to eat together, argued about what to watch on television – just one, in the sitting room – and gathered around the radio on a Sunday to listen to 'Round the Horn', 'the Navy Lark' and 'Two Way Family Favourites'. If that seemed a tad staid in this new swinging era, you could always tune in to Radio Caroline, broadcasting pop music from a ship located in international waters, which had the added frisson of being illegal. Caroline was the first of many and, as far as the younger generation were concerned, pirate radio ruled the airwaves.

PROTEST AND PEACE

While Dr Beeching was intent on closing railway lines, the Mini was king of the road, but every Easter, thousands of people used their own two feet to march from Aldermaston to London. These were the CND, Ban the Bomb marches, part of an era of protest and demonstrations. Folk were keen to stand up and be counted, but anger and indignation were not the only spirits lurking in the ether. Flower power and the rise of all things psychedelic reached its apotheosis in the summer of love, 1967. Fifty years ago, San Francisco seemed farther away than it does now, but the happenings there were mirrored here and, with the relaxation of many social taboos, happy hippies practised peace and love to their heart's content.

Websites

historic-uk.com
nationalarchives.gov.uk
reminiscethis.co.uk
the60sofficialsite.com

Folklore and FESTIVALS

Throughout the year, groups of people around the country, often strangely dressed, can be observed indulging in bizarre behaviour to the uproarious delight of enthusiastic onlookers. A good day out is to be had if you can suspend your disbelief and join in.

As well as customs and events that have become so deeply embedded in the national psyche that we think of them as part of the annual round – Guy Fawkes night, May Day – many others continue to flourish. Mummers still perform through village streets, wells are dressed in the Malvern Hills and elsewhere, and the unmistakable jingle of bells means the Morris men have arrived to entertain summer crowds. These islands are a veritable hotbed of quirky practices and offbeat celebrations, often dating back hundreds of years and more.

At Abbots Bromley in Staffordshire the annual Horn Dance is a sight to see. Six ancient wooden deer heads with real reindeer horns attached are carried by Deer Men wearing traditional costume. Together with a Fool, a Bowman, a Hobby Horse and Maid Marion (played by a man) they perform their age-old dance to music provided by a melodion player, progressing around the village, local farms and pubs. Wakes Monday is the day – the first or second Monday in September. Wakes week was the traditional holiday time in what was once the industrial north of England.

> *" They perform their age-old dance to music provided by a melodion player. "*

LEGENDARY LOCATIONS

Places at the centre of folk tales are often known for their special ambiance, for who frequented them or for a particular mysterious event. They all reward a visit (check opening times and facilities, where necessary). Here are just a few.

■ Glastonbury (Somerset) – legends abound! Reputedly the site of King Arthur's Camelot, and visited by Joseph of Arimathea. St Michael's Tower on the Tor is undoubtedly atmospheric.

■ Rendlesham Forest (Suffolk) – site of a well-documented visitation by an alien craft. A UFO trail has been laid out by the Forestry Commission.

■ Pluckley (Kent) – known as the most haunted village in England. You can go on ghost hunts and sleepovers. It's very popular at Halloween.

■ Sherwood Forest (Notts) – the thousand-year-old Major Oak in Birkland Wood near Edwinstowe is noted as the Merry Men's meeting place, just a ten-minute walk from the visitor centre.

■ Knaresborough (Yorks) – home of famous fortune-teller, prophetess and witch, Mother Shipton. Enter her cave and see the petrifying well that turns objects to stone.

■ West Wycombe (Bucks) – the neo-classical mansion is run by the National Trust. The caves, privately owned and open to the public, were the venue for Sir Francis Dashwood's notorious Hellfire Club. Creepy and supposedly haunted – visit if you dare!

ANNUAL EVENTS

The summer and winter solstices and midsummer day (24 June) are often marked locally, and St Bartholomew's Day (24 August) remains a traditional day for fairs and markets. May Day or early May bank holiday celebrations include Padstow's Obby Oss (Cornwall) and the Jack-in-the-Green festival, Hastings (East Sussex). Some local events continue an unbroken thread and some have been revived while others are relatively new. These are just a few among hundreds that take place all over the country.

■ Planting of the Penny Hedge, Whitby (Yorks); every year since 1159, according to legend, a woven hedge is constructed on the water's edge, strong enough to withstand three tides; the day before Ascension Day.

■ Oak Apple Day, London and Castleton (Derbyshire); Chelsea Pensioners parade to mark the anniversary of the restoration of the monarchy in 1660; a Garland King and Queen ride through Castleton accompanied by a band and Morris dancers; 29 May.

■ Thaxted Morris Meet (Essex); sides from all over the country come together to put on exuberant displays; three days in May/June.

■ Blessing of the Sea and Fisheries, Folkestone (Kent); a musical procession winds through the town to the harbour; nearest Sunday to St Peter's Day (29 June).

■ Durham Miners' Gala; brass bands, historic silk banners; second Saturday in July.

■ Widdecombe Fair (Devon), complete with Uncle Tom Cobleigh; second Tuesday in September.

■ Nottingham Goose Fair; first Thursday in October.

■ Alwinton Border Shepherds' Show (Northum); agricultural show with sheepdog trials, local wrestling, fell races, tug o' war and terrier racing; second Saturday in October.

■ Burning the Clocks, Brighton (East Sussex); enormous home-made paper clocks and lanterns are paraded through the streets to the beach and then burnt on a huge bonfire, with fireworks; 21 December.

■ Marshfield Paper Boys (Glos); mummers clad in costumes made from paper strips and streamers perform a traditional play through the streets; Boxing Day.

■ Hood Game, Haxey (Lincs); men in strange garb tussle for possession of various 'hoods', preceded and followed by elaborate rituals; St John's Eve (6 January).

■ Cheese-rolling at Cooper's Hill (Glos); participants chase an 8lb Double Gloucester cheese down a very steep slope in a series of races; late May bank holiday.

Venture to Whittlesea in Cambridgeshire in mid-January and you'll likely be amazed to come across a figure covered from head to toe in straw leading a procession of mummers, dancers and musicians. This is the Straw Bear Festival. Usually held over a weekend, it's a good way to brighten up what can be a gloomy time of year.

The straw bear can find his counterpart in Edinburgh at the August Ferry Fair, where the Burry Man comes out to play. An apparition covered in burrs, he was apparently the fall guy who paid the price for a poor fishing season, being expelled from town along with the bad luck. Now he collects money for charity.

FUN AND GAMES

Dover's Hill, a natural amphitheatre near Chipping Campden in Gloucestershire, has lovely views and is looked after by the National Trust. If you visit on the first Friday after the spring bank holiday, you'll get a taste of the first Olympic Games revival – the Cotswold Olimpiks, instigated in the early 17th century. The games were eventually abandoned in 1852 for lack of a venue but revived in 1951 for the Festival of Britain. They have been a more or less regular event at Dover's Hill since 1966, featuring an ever-popular 'sport' from way back – shin-kicking. Fortunately, the rules have been updated – no steel toecaps and plenty of straw padding. Who knows, you might even see some welly wanging and wheelbarrow racing, and you don't see that in a modern Olympic stadium.

" An apparition covered in burrs at the August Ferry Fair. "

Shrovetide football is another tradition that survives, bearing little resemblance to any league game you may have seen. In Ashbourne, Derbyshire, the game goes on for two days and the goals are three miles apart. Most of the action seems to take place in the river between those from north of the water, the Up'ards, and those from south of it, the Down'ards. Any number can take part and goals, unsurprisingly, are rare. Shrovetide is the Sunday, Monday and Tuesday before Ash Wednesday, so possibly a time of pre-Lent excess.

A gentler contest takes place at Tinsley Green in West Sussex.

Every Good Friday since 1932 (except 1942–45) the British and World Marbles championships have been held at the Greyhound pub, attracting teams from all over the world, although a marbles competition is said to have been played there in the time of Elizabeth I. That one was between two suitors for the hand of a fair maiden.

Websites

calendarcustoms.com
museumofbritishfolklore.com
nationaltrust.org.uk
themorrisring.org

Activity HOLIDAYS

Sunbathing lost its charm? Feeling restless after half an hour's lazing with a good book and a cocktail? If lounging around on holiday is just not cutting it any more, why not leap into action instead? An activity break could be just what you need.

How to make the most of precious time off is a question close to most people's hearts, and as a welcome change from the seaside or the museums and galleries of a city break, an activity holiday can provide the answer.

The choice is almost endless, from cycling, painting or pottery to horse-riding, trekking or white-water rafting, depending on how gentle or strenuous you

want your break to be. Are you interested in nature, history, food? Do you want to learn a new skill, explore new places, be adventurous? Whatever tickles your fancy, you'll be catered for, and not just in the UK. The world awaits, and whether you decide to go as a family, with friends or on your own, you're sure to be mixing with a group of like-minded people, all as keen as you are to enjoy themselves.

GIVE IT A TRY

Of course, it may be that you can't persuade friends or family to devote a whole week to one activity, and prefer not to tackle it among people you don't know. Plenty of places offer a whole range of activities, lasting from an hour or two to a full day, as well as catering for those who just want to do nothing much. Whatever your special interest may be, there'll be somewhere

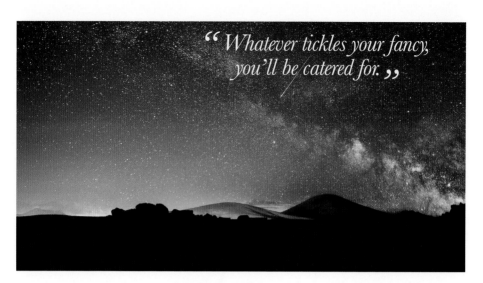

" Whatever tickles your fancy, you'll be catered for. "

you can indulge it. Like to try your hand at glass painting? No problem. You can make candles, jewellery or your own cosmetics, visit historic sites, go whale-watching, or learn how to play bridge or windsurf – or both.

OLD CRAFTS

If the idea of learning an oldfashioned country craft appeals, you could try hedge laying, woodland coppicing or hurdling (making a woven fence) among other rural skills.

Dry-stone walls have been a feature of the British landscape for well over three thousand years. They are beautiful to behold and provide a valuable habitat for a variety of flora and fauna, but it takes skill and patience to construct one. The Dry Stone Walling Association, a charitable organisation, runs weekends for beginners.

OOH LA LA!

While taking time out to pursue your favourite hobby is a great way to relax, discovering a new creative skill is fun, too. For an added frisson, why not consider learning something new in the appropriate country? You could try flamenco or salsa dancing in Spain, a wine course in France, cooking in Rome or Tuscany. You can even go on a language break – where better to learn French than in France with no humdrum distractions? *Quelle bonne idée!*

Specialist painting and photography holidays are not hard to find, world wide, and wellbeing breaks really do live up to their name.

WORK IT OUT

Working holidays can give you the added satisfaction of doing something worthwhile in your leisure time. Whether you opt to help clear invasive species from woodlands and ponds, clean beaches, repair footpaths or survey an area for bats and butterflies, conservation lies at their heart.

Websites

dswa.org.uk
golearnto.com
hfholidays.co.uk
nationaltrust.org.uk
naturetrek.co.uk
pgl.co.uk
vidados.com

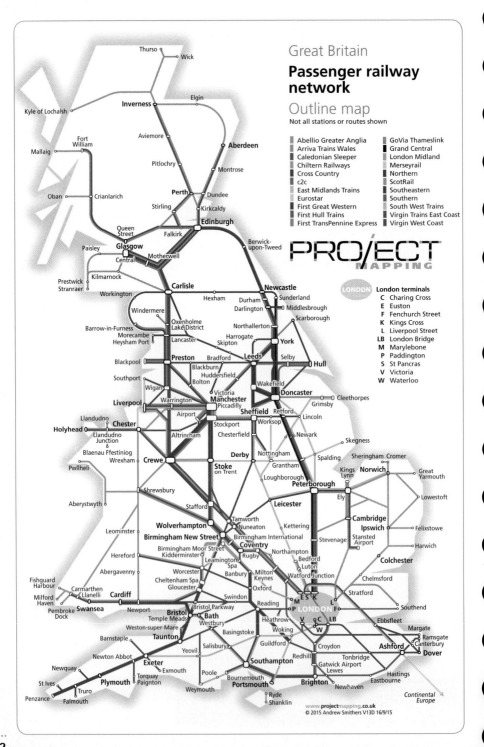

Great Britain
Passenger railway network
Outline map
Not all stations or routes shown

Abellio Greater Anglia
Arriva Trains Wales
Caledonian Sleeper
Chiltern Railways
Cross Country
c2c
East Midlands Trains
Eurostar
First Great Western
First Hull Trains
First TransPennine Express

GoVia Thameslink
Grand Central
London Midland
Merseyrail
Northern
ScotRail
Southeastern
Southern
South West Trains
Virgin Trains East Coast
Virgin West Coast

London terminals
C   Charing Cross
E   Euston
F   Fenchurch Street
K   Kings Cross
L   Liverpool Street
LB London Bridge
M   Marylebone
P   Paddington
S   St Pancras
V   Victoria
W   Waterloo

www.projectmapping.co.uk
© 2015 Andrew Smithers V13D 16/9/15

December

26 Monday

Boxing Day
Bank Holiday, UK

27 Tuesday

Bank Holiday, UK

28 Wednesday

29 Thursday

● *New Moon*

30 Friday

M	T	W	T	F	S	S	M	T	W	T	F	S	S
2	3	4	5	6	7	8	9	10	11	12	13	14	15

December
Week 52

Saturday **31**
New Year's Eve

JANUARY 2017 Sunday **1**
New Year's Day

New Year Chai Martini

Chai latte teabags 2
Granulated sugar 4 tsp or to taste
Single cream 100ml (3½fl oz)
Vanilla vodka 100ml (3½fl oz)
Ice cubes 16
Cinnamon for sprinkling

1 Place teabags into a heatproof measuring jug and pour in 100ml (3½fl oz) boiling water. Leave to brew for 5 minutes.
2 Remove teabags, add sugar and stir until dissolved. Pour in cream and vanilla vodka and leave to cool.
3 Place half the ice in a cocktail shaker and pour in half the liquid. Shake well then strain into two martini glasses. Repeat with remaining liquid and ice. Sprinkle with cinnamon and serve immediately.

Serves 2	Time 10 mins	Calories 239	Salt 0g	Fat 10g of which
V	plus cooling	Fibre 0g	Sugar 9.5g	6.1g is saturated

January

2 Monday
Bank Holiday, UK

3 Tuesday
Bank Holiday, Scotland

4 Wednesday

5 Thursday
) *First Quarter*

6 Friday
Epiphany

M	T	W	T	F	S	S	M	T	W	T	F	S	S
9	10	11	12	13	14	15	16	17	18	19	20	21	22

January
Week 1

Saturday 7

Sunday 8

Pork with Apple & Sage Sauce

Butter 25g (1oz)
Onion 1, peeled and chopped
Caster sugar 1 tsp
Cooking apple 1, peeled, cored and chopped
Dried sage 1 tsp
Worcestershire sauce ½ tsp
Olive oil for greasing
Pork chops 2
Baby vegetables and chips to serve, optional

1 Preheat oven to 200°C/180°fan/Gas 6. Melt butter in a saucepan, add onion and sugar and cook gently for 5-7 minutes until soft. Add apple, sage and 5 tbsp water and cook gently for 10-15 minutes until softened to a sauce. Season and add Worcestershire sauce.
2 Grease a griddle or frying pan and cook pork chops for 8-10 minutes on each side until cooked through.
3 Serve chops with sauce, chips and baby vegetables, if using.

Serves 2	Time 30 mins	Calories 533	Salt 0.5g	Fat 43g of which
		Fibre 2.5g	Sugar 11g	19g is saturated

57

January

9 Monday

10 Tuesday

11 Wednesday

12 Thursday

○ *Full Moon*

13 Friday

M	T	W	T	F	S	S	M	T	W	T	F	S	S
16	17	18	19	20	21	22	23	24	25	26	27	28	29

January
Week 2

Saturday **14**

Sunday **15**

Spiced Sweet Potato Soup

Butter 15g (½oz)
Onion 1, peeled and sliced
Sweet potato 1 large, peeled and cut into even-sized chunks
Parsnip 1, peeled and sliced
Swede 175g (6oz), peeled and diced
Balti paste 1 tbsp
Vegetable stock 900ml (1½ pints)
Crème fraîche and naan bread to serve, optional

1 In a large saucepan melt butter over a low heat and add onion. Put on lid and sweat onion for 5 minutes or until soft.
2 Increase heat slightly and add vegetables and balti paste. Cook, stirring, for 2 minutes. Stir in 800ml (28fl oz) stock and bring to the boil. Simmer for 20 minutes or until vegetables are soft.
3 Remove from the heat, puree with a hand-held blender, add a little more stock, if needed, and season to taste. Serve with naan and topped with a spoonful of crème fraîche if you like.

Serves 4	Time 35 mins	Calories 116	Salt 2.1g	Fat 4.6g of which
V F		Fibre 4.3g	Sugar 0g	2.1g is saturated

January

16 Monday

17 Tuesday

18 Wednesday

19 Thursday

(*Last Quarter*

20 Friday

M	T	W	T	F	S	S	M	T	W	T	F	S	S
23	24	25	26	27	28	29	30	31	1	2	3	4	5

January
Week 3

Saturday **21**

Sunday **22**

Chicken & Leek Gratin

Vegetable oil 1 tbsp
Leeks 2, washed and sliced
Butter 15g (½oz)
Plain flour 15g (½oz)
Milk 300ml (½ pint)
Chicken breast 1, chopped
Snipped chives 2 tbsp
Small French stick 1, sliced
Whole grain mustard 1 tbsp
Cheddar cheese 50g (2oz)

1 Heat oil in a large saucepan and gently fry leeks for 5 minutes or until soft.
2 Put butter, flour and milk into a saucepan and heat, whisking continuously, until sauce boils and is smooth. Season to taste.
3 Preheat grill to hot. Stir white sauce, chicken and chives into leeks and cook gently, stirring, for 5 minutes or until chicken is cooked. Toast bread on both sides then spread with mustard.
4 Spoon mixture into a small baking dish, top with toasts (mustard side up) and cheese and grill for 3 minutes.

Serves 2	Time 30 mins	Calories 712	Salt 2.3g	Fat 27g of which
		Fibre 8.5g	Sugar 1.8g	12g is saturated

January

23 Monday

24 Tuesday

25 Wednesday

Burns' Night

26 Thursday

27 Friday

M	T	W	T	F	S	S	M	T	W	T	F	S	S
30	31	1	2	3	4	5	6	7	8	9	10	11	12

January
Week 4

Saturday 28

● *New Moon*

Sunday 29

Crispy Duck Salad

**Half aromatic crispy duck
(including pancakes and hoisin
sauce)** 530g/800g pack
Toasted sesame oil 3 tsp
White wine vinegar 1 tbsp
Sesame seeds 1 tbsp
Olive oil 2 tbsp
Bistro salad 180g pack

1 Cook duck according to pack's
instructions.
2 Meanwhile, whisk hoisin with
2 tsp sesame oil and vinegar.
3 Toast sesame seeds for 2
minutes in a dry frying pan.
4 Roll pancakes up together and
cut into 1cm (½in) slices. Heat
remaining sesame oil with olive
oil in frying pan and fry pancakes
for 4-5 minutes until golden.
5 Mix pancake ribbons into
salad leaves and divide between
plates. Sprinkle with half the
dressing. Shred duck with forks
and place on top of salad leaves.
Sprinkle with sesame seeds
and serve immediately with
remaining dressing.

Serves 3-4	Time 45 mins	Calories 480	Salt 0.4g	Fat 20g of which
		Fibre 1.1g	Sugar 1.4g	1.5g is saturated

January

30 Monday

31 Tuesday

1 Wednesday FEBRUARY

2 Thursday

3 Friday

M	T	W	T	F	S	S	M	T	W	T	F	S	S
6	7	8	9	10	11	12	13	14	15	16	17	18	19

February
Week 5

Saturday 4
) *First Quarter*

Sunday 5

Cauliflower 'Rice'

Cauliflower 1, broken into florets
Ground coriander 1 tsp
Olive oil 1 tbsp
Chopped mint 2-3 tbsp

1 Preheat oven to 200°C/180°fan/Gas 6. Place cauliflower florets into a food processor and pulse several times to give a rice-like texture.
2 Season well and mix with coriander and oil, then spread on a baking sheet. Bake for 10-12 minutes until it has a dry but fluffy texture.
3 Stir in mint, season to taste and serve alongside your chosen fish or meat and vegetables.

Serves 3-4	Time 15 mins	Calories 76	Salt 0g	Fat 3.6g of which
V		Fibre 3.3g	Sugar 0g	0.5g is saturated

65

February

M	T	W	T	F	S	S	M	T	W	T	F	S	S
30	31	1	2	3	4	5	6	7	8	9	10	11	12

6 Monday

Accession of Queen Elizabeth II

7 Tuesday

8 Wednesday

9 Thursday

10 Friday

M	T	W	T	F	S	S	M	T	W	T	F	S	S
13	14	15	16	17	18	19	20	21	22	23	24	25	26

February
Week 6

Saturday 11
○ *Full Moon*

Sunday 12
Septuagesima Sunday

Savoury Bacon & Herb Loaf

Streaky bacon 50g (2oz), chopped
Onion 1, peeled and finely chopped
Celery 2 sticks, chopped
Self-raising flour 225g (8oz)
Butter 25g (1oz), softened
Milk 150ml (¼ pint)
Egg 1, beaten
Chopped parsley 1 tbsp
Dried mixed herbs ½ tsp

1 Preheat oven to 180°C/160°fan/Gas 4. Grease a 450g (1lb) loaf tin or 16cm (6in) cake tin.
2 Dry fry bacon in a frying pan for 2 minutes, then add onion and celery and cook for 5 minutes until soft.
3 Sift flour and ½ tsp salt into a bowl and rub in butter.
4 In a jug mix milk with egg and herbs and season. Add to dry ingredients with bacon mixture and mix together. Spoon into tin and bake for 50-60 minutes until risen and golden. Cool on a rack.

Serves 4	Time 1 hr	Calories 327	Salt 1.7g	Fat 11g of which
F	10 mins	Fibre 3.5g	Sugar 0g	5.2g is saturated

February

M	T	W	T	F	S	S	M	T	W	T	F	S	S
6	7	8	9	10	11	12	13	14	15	16	17	18	19

13 Monday

14 Tuesday
St Valentine's Day

15 Wednesday

16 Thursday

17 Friday

M	T	W	T	F	S	S	M	T	W	T	F	S	S
20	21	22	23	24	25	26	27	28	1	2	3	4	5

February
Week 7

Saturday 18
☾ *Last Quarter*

Sunday 19

Mini Beef Roast with Chipotle Butter

Unsalted butter 50g (2oz), softened
Chopped flat-leaf parsley 1 tbsp
Chipotle paste 2 tsp
Beef mini roast 1 x 400-450g (14oz-1lb)
Chips and steamed vegetables or salad to serve, optional

1 Preheat oven to 190°C/170°fan/Gas 5. Mix together butter, parsley and chipotle paste.
2 Place beef joint on a chopping board, make several slashes over surface, season and spread with butter. Transfer to a roasting rack in a medium non-stick roasting tin and roast for 40-50 minutes (for medium). Cover with foil if browning too quickly.
3 Remove from oven, transfer to a warm plate, cover and leave to rest for 5-10 minutes. Slice and serve with any meat juices, chips and seasonal vegetables or salad, if you like.

Serves 2	Time 1 hr	Calories 770	Salt 0.5g	Fat 66g of which
F		Fibre 0.7g	Sugar 0g	33g is saturated

February

20 Monday

21 Tuesday

22 Wednesday

23 Thursday

24 Friday

M	T	W	T	F	S	S	M	T	W	T	F	S	S
27	28	1	2	3	4	5	6	7	8	9	10	11	12

February
Week 8

Saturday 25

Sunday 26
● *New Moon*
Quinquagesima Sunday

Easy Peasy Danish Pastries

Ready-rolled puff pastry 375g packet
Egg 1, beaten
Apple sauce 8 tsp
Marzipan 110g (4oz)
Apricot jam 2 tbsp, warmed
Toasted flaked almonds 2 tbsp

1 Preheat oven to 220°C/200°fan/Gas 7. Line a baking tray with baking paper.
2 Unroll pastry and cut into eight squares. Brush each with egg and place 1 tsp apple sauce in centre. Roll marzipan into a sausage shape about 5cm (2in) long and cut into eight. Place each piece onto apple sauce. Fold up corners of pastry to meet in middle. Brush with egg and place on tray.
3 Bake for 15-18 minutes until risen and golden.
4 Brush with jam and sprinkle with almonds. Serve warm.

Makes 8
V F

Time 30 mins

Calories 272
Fibre 2g

Salt 0.4g
Sugar 14g

Fat 16g of which 6.3g is saturated

February

M	T	W	T	F	S	S	M	T	W	T	F	S	S
20	21	22	23	24	25	26	**27**	**28**	**1**	**2**	**3**	**4**	**5**

27 Monday

28 Tuesday

Shrove Tuesday

1 Wednesday MARCH

St David's Day
Ash Wednesday

2 Thursday

3 Friday

M	T	W	T	F	S	S	M	T	W	T	F	S	S
6	7	8	9	10	11	12	13	14	15	16	17	18	19

March
Week 9

Saturday 4

Sunday 5

❭ *First Quarter*
Quadragesima Sunday

Buttermilk Pancakes with Bacon & Syrup

Plain flour 110g (4oz)
Baking powder 2 tsp
Bicarbonate of soda ½ tsp
Caster sugar 1 tbsp
Salt ½ tsp
Eggs 2 large, beaten
Buttermilk 284ml pot
Butter 25g (1oz), melted, plus extra for frying
Streaky bacon 8 rashers
Maple syrup to serve

1 Sift flour, baking powder and bicarbonate of soda into a bowl. Stir in sugar and salt. Whisk in eggs, buttermilk and butter, taking care not to over-whisk.
2 Heat a non-stick frying pan and add a small amount of butter. Pour in a ladleful of batter and cook for 2-3 minutes, until bubbles appear and edges start to turn dry. Flip and cook for 1 minute more, until golden underneath. Keep warm. Repeat until batter is used up.
3 Place bacon rashers side-by-side in a large non-stick frying

Serves 4	Time 45 mins	Calories 367	Salt 3.2g	Fat 18g of which
		Fibre 1.1g	Sugar 14g	7.7g is saturated

pan. Fry over a medium heat for 5-6 minutes, turning halfway through, until crisp.

4 Serve pancakes topped with bacon rashers and drizzled with maple syrup.

March

M	T	W	T	F	S	S	M	T	W	T	F	S	S
27	28	1	2	3	4	5	6	7	8	9	10	11	12

6 Monday

7 Tuesday

8 Wednesday

9 Thursday

10 Friday

M	T	W	T	F	S	S	M	T	W	T	F	S	S
13	14	15	16	17	18	19	20	21	22	23	24	25	26

March
Week 10

Saturday 11

Sunday 12
○ *Full Moon*

Marinated Fish Steaks with Mushrooms

Teriyaki marinade 6 tbsp
Lemon ½, finely grated zest and juice
Chilli powder ¼ tsp
Tuna, cod or halibut steaks 4 x 200g (7oz)
New potatoes 400g (14oz), sliced
Butter 40g (1½oz)
Button mushrooms 250g (9oz), wiped and halved
Spring onions 6, trimmed and sliced lengthways
Chopped coriander 4 tbsp

1 Mix teriyaki marinade, lemon zest and juice and chilli powder in a shallow dish. Add fish steaks and turn until evenly coated. Cover and leave to marinate while cooking potatoes.
2 Steam new potato slices for 15 minutes or until just tender.
3 Meanwhile, melt half the butter in a large frying pan, add mushrooms and cook gently for 3-4 minutes until soft. Remove and keep warm.

Serves 4	Time 30 mins	Calories 394	Salt 0.9g	Fat 10g of which
		Fibre 3.5g	Sugar 8.1g	5.7g is saturated

4 Add remaining butter to frying pan and cook fish with marinade for 2-3 minutes on each side until cooked through. Remove and keep warm.

5 Add spring onions to pan juices and cook for 3-4 minutes until soft. Mix in potatoes, mushrooms and coriander and serve with fish steaks.

75

March

13 Monday

14 Tuesday

15 Wednesday

16 Thursday

17 Friday

St Patrick's Day
Bank Holiday, N Ireland

M	T	W	T	F	S	S	M	T	W	T	F	S	S
20	21	22	23	24	25	26	27	28	29	30	31	1	2

March
Week 11

Saturday **18**

Sunday **19**

Chocolate Key Lime Pies

Butter 40g (1½oz)
Oreo cookies 154g packet, crushed
Condensed milk 397g can
Eggs 2 large, separated
Limes 2, finely grated zest and juice
Green food colouring a few drops, optional
Caster sugar 50g (2oz)

1 Melt butter in a saucepan then stir in cookie crumbs. Spoon into 6 ovenproof ramekins. Chill for 10 minutes. Preheat oven to 180°C/160°fan/Gas 4.
2 Beat condensed milk with egg yolks, lime zest and juice and colouring, if using. Pour onto biscuit bases and place on a baking tray. Bake for 15 minutes or until set.
3 Whisk egg whites until softly stiff. Gradually whisk in sugar. Pile meringue onto pies and return to oven for 5 minutes or until tops are golden. Serve warm or cold.

Serves 6	**Time** 35 mins	**Calories** 435	**Salt** 0.5g	**Fat** 19g of which
V		**Fibre** 0.8g	**Sugar** 45g	10g is saturated

March

M	T	W	T	F	S	S	M	T	W	T	F	S	S
13	14	15	16	17	18	19	20	21	22	23	24	25	26

20 Monday

☾ *Last Quarter*
Vernal equinox
Spring begins

21 Tuesday

22 Wednesday

23 Thursday

24 Friday

M	T	W	T	F	S	S	M	T	W	T	F	S	S
27	28	29	30	31	1	2	3	4	5	6	7	8	9

March
Week 12

Saturday 25

Don't forget to put your clocks forward 1 hour tonight

Sunday 26

British Summer Time begins
Mothering Sunday
Fourth Sunday in Lent

Decadent Red Velvet Cake

Unsalted butter 475g (1lb 1oz)
Caster sugar 250g (9oz)
Eggs 3 large, separated
Vanilla extract 2 tsp
White wine vinegar 1 tsp
Specialist cake decorator's red food colouring paste 1 tsp
Cocoa powder 1½ tbsp
Bicarbonate of soda 1 tsp
Self-raising flour 275g (10oz)
Buttermilk 284ml pot
Icing sugar 425g (15oz)
Full fat soft cheese 180g tub

Slices 16	Time 1¾ hrs	Calories 500	Salt 0.5g	Fat 29g of which
V		Fibre 1g	Sugar 44g	18g is saturated

1 Preheat oven to 180°C/160°fan/Gas 4. Grease and line a round deep 20cm (8in) tin.
2 In a large bowl cream together 250g (9oz) butter and caster sugar until pale and fluffy. Beat in egg yolks, vanilla, vinegar and colouring. Sift in cocoa, bicarbonate and half the flour, then mix in half the buttermilk.
3 Mix in remaining flour and buttermilk. In a separate bowl whisk egg whites until foamy then fold into cake mixture.

4 Spoon into tin and bake for 50 minutes or until a skewer comes out clean. Cool in tin until cold.
5 Level top and cut in half horizontally, reserving crumbs.

Beat together icing sugar, remaining butter and cheese. Use to sandwich cake together and spread around sides and top. Sprinkle with cake crumbs.

March

27 Monday

28 Tuesday

● *New Moon*

29 Wednesday

30 Thursday

31 Friday

M	T	W	T	F	S	S	M	T	W	T	F	S	S
3	4	5	6	7	8	9	10	11	12	13	14	15	16

April
Week 13

APRIL **Saturday 1**

Sunday 2

Slow Cooked Lamb with Rhubarb

Lean lamb shoulder, neck fillet or leg 675g (1½lb), cubed
Dried mixed herbs ½ tsp
Sunflower oil 1 tbsp
Onions 2 small, peeled and cut into wedges
Lamb stock 600ml (1 pint)
Runny honey 2 tsp
Rhubarb 1-2 sticks, chopped
Frozen peas 75g (3oz)
Chopped parsley and mint 1 tbsp of each, optional
Mash and vegetables to serve, optional

1 Preheat oven to 170°C/150°fan/Gas 3. Season lamb with salt, pepper and dried mixed herbs.
2 Heat oil in a large non-stick frying pan and cook lamb for 5-7 minutes until browned all over. With a slotted spoon transfer to a large casserole dish.
3 Cook onions in frying pan for 3-4 minutes. Add stock and honey, bring to the boil then transfer to casserole. Bake in

Serves 6	Time 1¾ hrs	Calories 281	Salt 1.5g	Fat 18g of which
F		Fibre 2.3g	Sugar 4g	7.6g is saturated

oven for 1 hour 20 minutes.
4 Add rhubarb and peas and return to oven for 10 minutes.

5 Garnish with herbs, if using, and serve with mash and seasonal vegetables, if you like.

April

M	T	W	T	F	S	S	M	T	W	T	F	S	S
27	28	29	30	31	1	2	3	4	5	6	7	8	9

3 Monday
❭ *First Quarter*

4 Tuesday

5 Wednesday

6 Thursday

7 Friday

M	T	W	T	F	S	S	M	T	W	T	F	S	S
10	11	12	13	14	15	16	17	18	19	20	21	22	23

April
Week 14

Saturday **8**

Sunday **9**
Palm Sunday

Chocolate Lollipops

White chocolate 200g bar, chopped
Lollipop sticks 8
Giant chocolate buttons 10-11
White mini marshmallows 50g (2oz)
Black and pink gel food colour to decorate

1 Using the base of a mug, draw eight circles on a sheet of baking paper. Turn over paper and weight each corner.

2 Melt chocolate in a heatproof bowl set over a pan of barely simmering water.

3 Spoon chocolate onto drawn circles. Place a lollipop stick onto each, turning once to coat. Place a button onto each circle near stick and snip remaining buttons into ear shapes and place one on each side of each button. Snip marshmallows in half with scissors and gently push into chocolate in concentric circles. Use gel to create eyes and mouth. Leave to set.

Serves 8	Time 45 mins	Calories 231	Salt 0.1g	Fat 12g of which
V	plus setting	Fibre 0.3g	Sugar 22g	7.4g is saturated

April

M	T	W	T	F	S	S	M	T	W	T	F	S	S
3	4	5	6	7	8	9	10	11	12	13	14	15	16

10 Monday

11 Tuesday

○ *Full Moon*

12 Wednesday

13 Thursday

14 Friday

Good Friday
Bank Holiday, UK

M	T	W	T	F	S	S	M	T	W	T	F	S	S
17	18	19	20	21	22	23	24	25	26	27	28	29	30

April
Week 15

Saturday 15

Sunday 16
Easter Day

Easter Spice Cake

Butter 175g (6oz), softened
Caster sugar 175g (6oz)
Eggs 2 large, beaten
Baking powder 1 tsp
Ground cinnamon 1 tsp
Allspice 1 tsp
Self-raising flour 300g (11oz)
Vanilla extract 1 tsp
Milk 225ml (8fl oz)
Marzipan 175g (6oz)
Lemon curd 75g (3oz)
Mini eggs to decorate, optional

1 Preheat oven to 190°C/170°fan/Gas 5. Grease and line 3x18cm (7in) sandwich tins.
2 In a large bowl cream butter and caster sugar together until pale and fluffy. Gradually beat in eggs, then sift in baking powder, cinnamon, allspice and half the flour. Mix in vanilla extract and half the milk. Repeat with remaining flour and milk.
3 Divide mixture between sandwich tins and bake for 20 minutes or until firm to touch. Cool in tins.

Slices 12	Time 40 mins	Calories 349	Salt 0.7g	Fat 16g of which
V F	plus cooling	Fibre 1.5g	Sugar 27g	8.4g is saturated

4 Cut marzipan into 2 pieces and roll out into 18cm (7in) circles. Sandwich cakes together with marzipan and curd. If you like, use a little curd to fix marzipan and eggs to the top.

April

	M	T	W	T	F	S	S	M	T	W	T	F	S	S
	10	11	12	13	14	15	16	**17**	**18**	**19**	20	21	22	23

17 Monday

Easter Monday
Bank Holiday, England, Wales and N Ireland

18 Tuesday

19 Wednesday

☾ *Last Quarter*

20 Thursday

21 Friday

Birthday of Queen Elizabeth II

M	T	W	T	F	S	S	M	T	W	T	F	S	S
24	25	26	27	28	29	30	1	2	3	4	5	6	7

April
Week 16

Saturday 22

Sunday 23

St George's Day
Low Sunday

Rhubarb, Ginger & Custard Tart

Butter 40g (1½oz), cubed
Caster sugar 50g (2oz)
Self-raising flour 110g (4oz)
Egg yolk 1
Milk 2-3 tbsp
Rhubarb 275g (10oz), chopped
Stem ginger 1 piece, drained and finely chopped
Custard 275g (10oz)

1 Place butter, 25g (1oz) sugar and flour in a food processor and pulse until it resembles fine breadcrumbs. Add egg yolk and milk 1 tbsp at a time, and pulse to give a soft dough. Knead, then chill for 45 minutes.

2 Place rhubarb in a saucepan with ginger, remaining sugar and 2 tbsp water. Cover and bring to the boil, then simmer gently for 5 minutes until it's soft and pulpy, stirring occasionally.

3 Preheat oven to 190°C/170°fan/Gas 5. On a floured surface, roll out pastry and use to line a 20cm (8in) loose-based flan tin.

Serves 6	Time 40 mins	Calories 208	Salt 0.3g	Fat 8.2g of which
V F	plus chilling	Fibre 1.6g	Sugar 13g	4.8g is saturated

4 Spread custard over pastry base and top with cooked rhubarb and ginger. Bake for 20 minutes or until pastry is golden. Leave in tin until cold then slice and serve.

87

April

M	T	W	T	F	S	S	M	T	W	T	F	S	S
17	18	19	20	21	22	23	24	25	26	27	28	29	30

24 Monday

25 Tuesday

26 Wednesday

● *New Moon*

27 Thursday

28 Friday

M	T	W	T	F	S	S	M	T	W	T	F	S	S
1	2	3	4	5	6	7	8	9	10	11	12	13	14

April
Week 17

Saturday **29**

Sunday **30**

Liver with Balsamic-Glazed Shallots

Olive or sunflower oil 1 tbsp
Shallots 350g (12oz), peeled, halved if large
Light muscovado (or granulated) sugar 4 tsp
Balsamic vinegar 2 tbsp
Frozen chicken livers 500g (1lb 2oz), defrosted
Butter 50g (2oz)
Fresh sage leaves small bunch or 1 tsp dried
Closed cup mushrooms 150g (5oz), wiped and sliced
Sherry, red wine or chicken stock 4 tbsp
Mash and steamed cabbage to serve (optional)

1 Heat oil in a large frying pan over a medium heat and stir-fry shallots for 5 minutes until beginning to soften. Sprinkle with sugar, add vinegar and fry for another 5 minutes, turning frequently, until caramelised.
2 Put livers in a sieve, rinse then drain. Cut into large chunks, discarding any white cores.

3 Add butter and sage to pan and when butter has melted add livers and mushrooms and fry for 3–4 minutes until browned but still slightly pink inside.

4 Stir in sherry, red wine or chicken stock, season and cook for 1 minute. Then serve with mash and steamed cabbage, if you like.

Serves 4	Time 20 mins	Calories 295	Salt 0.5g	Fat 16g of which
		Fibre 1.9g	Sugar 6g	7.8g is saturated

May

M	T	W	T	F	S	S	M	T	W	T	F	S	S
24	25	26	27	28	29	30	1	2	3	4	5	6	7

1 Monday MAY

Bank Holiday, UK

2 Tuesday

3 Wednesday

> *First Quarter*

4 Thursday

5 Friday

M	T	W	T	F	S	S	M	T	W	T	F	S	S
8	9	10	11	12	13	14	15	16	17	18	19	20	21

May
Week 18

Saturday 6

Sunday 7

British Asparagus & Goat's Cheese Tartlets

Ready-rolled puff pastry 320g pack
Plain flour 1 tbsp
British asparagus 8-10 spears, trimmed and cut into 5cm (2in) pieces
Sun-dried tomatoes 75g (3oz), drained and chopped, plus 1 tbsp of oil from jar
Goat's cheese 125g (4½oz), crumbled
Rocket and balsamic vinegar to serve

1 Preheat oven to 230°C/210°fan/Gas 8. Cut pastry into four rectangles and place on a floured baking tray. Score edge of each with a sharp knife.
2 In a bowl mix asparagus with tomatoes and oil. Divide between pastry and top with cheese. Bake for 12-15 minutes until golden.
3 Toss some rocket in a little vinegar and place on top of tartlets. Serve immediately.

Serves 4	**Time** 30 mins	**Calories** 530	**Salt** 0.8g	**Fat** 39g of which
V		**Fibre** 3.6g	**Sugar** 0g	17g is saturated

May

8 Monday

9 Tuesday

10 Wednesday
○ *Full Moon*

11 Thursday

12 Friday

M	T	W	T	F	S	S	M	T	W	T	F	S	S
15	16	17	18	19	20	21	22	23	24	25	26	27	28

May
Week 19

Saturday **13**

Sunday **14**

Frosty Top Lemon Loaf

Butter 50g (2oz), softened
Caster sugar 75g (3oz)
Self-raising flour 75g (3oz)
Ground almonds 25g (1oz)
Egg 1 large, beaten
Lemon ½, finely grated zest and juice
Granulated sugar 50g (2oz)

1 Preheat oven to 180°C/160°fan/Gas 4. Grease and line a 450g (1lb) loaf tin.
2 In a large bowl mix together butter, caster sugar, flour, ground almonds, egg and lemon zest. Spoon mixture into tin and bake for 35 minutes or until risen and firm to touch.
3 Mix lemon juice with sugar and spoon over cake as soon as it comes out of oven. Leave in tin to cool for at least 10 minutes before turning out onto a wire rack to cool completely.

Slices 10	**Time** 45 mins	**Calories** 136	**Salt** 0.2g	**Fat** 6.2g of which
V F		**Fibre** 0.3g	**Sugar** 13g	2.9g is saturated

93

May

M	T	W	T	F	S	S	M	T	W	T	F	S	S
8	9	10	11	12	13	14	15	16	17	18	19	20	21

15 Monday

16 Tuesday

17 Wednesday

18 Thursday

19 Friday

☾ *Last Quarter*

Saturday 20

Sunday 21
Rogation Sunday

Fruity Lamb Pilaff

Sunflower oil 1 tbsp
Lean diced lamb (neck fillet, shoulder or leg) 450g (1lb), seasoned
Onion 1, peeled and thinly sliced
Paprika 2 tsp
Hot vegetable stock 600ml (1 pint)
Cinnamon stick 1
Basmati rice 275g (10oz)
Dried apricots 50g (2oz), chopped
Chopped coriander and lemon wedges to serve, optional

1 Preheat oven to 180°C/160°fan/Gas 4.
2 Heat oil in a large non-stick frying pan and cook lamb for 6-8 minutes until golden brown. Spoon into a large casserole dish.
3 Add onion to frying pan with paprika and cook for 3-4 minutes until soft. Add stock and bring to the boil.
4 Pour stock and onion into casserole with cinnamon stick. Cover and bake for 1-1½ hours.

5 Stir in rice, cover and return to oven for 20-30 minutes until rice is cooked (check it occasionally and add more water if necessary).

6 Remove from oven, discard cinnamon stick and stir in apricots. Garnish with coriander and serve with lemon wedges, if using.

Serves 4	Time 2¼ hrs	Calories 531	Salt 2.4g	Fat 20g of which
		Fibre 3.8g	Sugar 0g	7.7g is saturated

M	T	W	T	F	S	S	M	T	W	T	F	S	S
15	16	17	18	19	20	21	**22**	**23**	**24**	**25**	**26**	**27**	**28**

22 Monday

23 Tuesday

24 Wednesday

25 Thursday
● *New Moon*
Ascension Day
Holy Thursday

26 Friday

Saturday **27**

Sunday **28**

British Asparagus & Salmon Thai Curry

Olive oil 1 tbsp
Garlic 2 cloves, peeled and crushed
Red onion 1, peeled and finely chopped
Red Thai curry paste 1 tbsp
Salmon fillets 4, cut into chunks
Coconut milk 400ml can
Fish or vegetable stock 250ml (9fl oz)
Fish sauce 1 tsp
Brown sugar 1 tsp
Lemon 1, juice only
British asparagus 2 bundles (approx. 500g/1lb 2oz), trimmed
Kaffir lime leaves 4
Jasmine rice and coriander leaves to serve, optional

1 Heat oil in a wok or large frying pan and cook garlic, onion and curry paste over a medium heat for 2 minutes.
2 Add salmon and stir well. Then add remaining ingredients (except rice and coriander). Cook gently for 10-15 minutes until asparagus and salmon are cooked. Season to taste, remove lime leaves and serve in bowls, sprinkled with coriander leaves, if you like. Serve jasmine rice in separate bowls.

Serves 4	**Time** 25 mins	**Calories** 500	**Salt** 0.9g	**Fat** 38g of which
F		**Fibre** 4.7g	**Sugar** 2.2g	18g is saturated

May

M	T	W	T	F	S	S	M	T	W	T	F	S	S
22	23	24	25	26	27	28	29	30	31	1	2	3	4

29 Monday
Bank Holiday, UK

30 Tuesday

31 Wednesday

1 Thursday JUNE
❭ *First Quarter*

2 Friday
Coronation Day

M	T	W	T	F	S	S	M	T	W	T	F	S	S
5	6	7	8	9	10	11	12	13	14	15	16	17	18

June
Week 22

Saturday 3

Sunday 4

Whit Sunday
Pentecost

Fruity Coronation Chicken

Low-fat natural fromage frais 2 tbsp
Light mayonnaise 1 tbsp
Mild curry paste 1 tsp
Mango chutney 2 tsp
Cooked chicken 225g (8oz), cut into chunks
Ripe peaches 2, cut into wedges
Mixed salad leaves 50g (2oz)
Toasted flaked almonds 2 tbsp
Poppadums 2, optional

1 Mix together fromage frais, mayonnaise, curry paste and chutney and season to taste. Stir into chicken along with peaches.
2 Place salad leaves on individual plates and top with chicken mixture. Sprinkle with almonds, and serve with poppadums, if using.

Serves 2	Time 10 mins	Calories 350	Salt 0.5g	Fat 15g of which
		Fibre 1.9g	Sugar 7g	1.9g is saturated

99

June

M	T	W	T	F	S	S	M	T	W	T	F	S	S
29	30	31	1	2	3	4	5	6	7	8	9	10	11

5 Monday

6 Tuesday

7 Wednesday

8 Thursday

9 Friday

○ *Full Moon*

M	T	W	T	F	S	S	M	T	W	T	F	S	S
12	13	14	15	16	17	18	19	20	21	22	23	24	25

June
Week 23

Saturday 10
Birthday of Prince Philip, Duke of Edinburgh

Sunday 11
Trinity Sunday

Luxury Egg & Cress Sandwiches

Eggs 4
Boursin cheese with black pepper 50g (2oz)
Light mayonnaise 3–4 tbsp
Wholemeal bread 8 slices
Salad cress a punnet

1 Hard boil eggs, cool and then shell.
2 Mash eggs with cheese and mayonnaise.
3 Take 4 slices of bread and spread filling over one side of each slice, scatter with snipped salad cress and pop remaining bread on top to make four sandwiches. Cut each one into four triangles and serve.

Makes 4	**Time** 15 mins	**Calories** 278	**Salt** 0.9g	**Fat** 13g of which
		Fibre 4.3g	**Sugar** 0.4g	3.1g is saturated

June

	M	T	W	T	F	S	S	M	T	W	T	F	S	S
	5	6	7	8	9	10	11	12	13	14	15	16	17	18

12 Monday

13 Tuesday

14 Wednesday

15 Thursday

Corpus Christi

16 Friday

M	T	W	T	F	S	S	M	T	W	T	F	S	S
19	20	21	22	23	24	25	26	27	28	29	30	1	2

June
Week 24

Saturday **17**

(*Last Quarter*

Sunday **18**

Father's Day

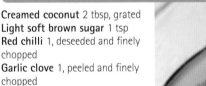

Spicy Beef Satay Sticks

Creamed coconut 2 tbsp, grated
Light soft brown sugar 1 tsp
Red chilli 1, deseeded and finely chopped
Garlic clove 1, peeled and finely chopped
Lime ½, juice only
Coriander large handful, chopped, plus extra to garnish
Lean beef sirloin, rump or topside steaks 450g (1lb), cut into 2.5cm (1in) cubes
Cooked pack of quinoa and rice to serve, optional

1 Mix all ingredients except beef in a shallow bowl. Season.
2 Thread beef cubes onto four short skewers, place into marinade and turn to coat cubes. Cover, chill and marinate for at least 20 minutes.
3 Cook according to preference (rare: 2½ minutes; medium: 4 minutes; well: 6 minutes on each side) on a barbecue, turning once. Serve with quinoa and rice and scattered with coriander.

Serves 4	Time 10 mins	Calories 214	Salt 0.2g	Fat 10g of which
F	plus chilling	Fibre 0.5g	Sugar 1.2g	6.7g is saturated

June

19 Monday

20 Tuesday

21 Wednesday

Summer solstice
Summer begins

22 Thursday

23 Friday

M	T	W	T	F	S	S	M	T	W	T	F	S	S
26	27	28	29	30	1	2	3	4	5	6	7	8	9

June
Week 25

Saturday 24

● *New Moon*

Sunday 25

French-Style Couscous with Prawns

Couscous 110g (4oz)
Sundried tomato paste 1 tbsp
Chicken stock 200ml (7fl oz), boiling
Cooked king prawns 150g pack
Tomatoes 2, diced
Cucumber 7cm (3in) piece, diced
Frozen peas 75g (3oz), cooked
Chopped mint 2-3 tbsp

1 Place couscous in a large bowl. Stir sundried tomato paste into stock and then pour onto couscous. Stir, cover, then leave for 5 minutes.
2 Fluff up couscous with a fork then leave to cool.
3 Stir in remaining ingredients, season to taste and serve immediately.

Serves 2	**Time** 15 mins plus cooling	**Calories** 310 **Fibre** 5.7g	**Salt** 1.8g **Sugar** 0g	**Fat** 2.2g of which 0.4g is saturated

June

	M	T	W	T	F	S	S	M	T	W	T	F	S	S
	19	20	21	22	23	24	25	26	27	28	29	30	1	2

26 Monday

27 Tuesday

28 Wednesday

29 Thursday

30 Friday

M	T	W	T	F	S	S	M	T	W	T	F	S	S
3	4	5	6	7	8	9	10	11	12	13	14	15	16

July
Week 26

JULY Saturday 1

> *First Quarter*

Sunday 2

Chocolate Mint Biscuit Bars

Butter 110g (4oz), softened
Caster sugar 110g (4oz)
Plain flour 175g (6oz)
Icing sugar 175g (6oz)
Peppermint extract ½ tsp
Dark chocolate 175g (6oz), chopped

1 Preheat oven to 180°C/160°fan/Gas 4 and grease a tin or dish 25cm x 17cm (10in x 7in). Cream butter and caster sugar together until pale and fluffy. Mix in flour and knead to a smooth dough. Press into tin, prick all over with a fork then bake for 15 minutes. Leave to cool in tin.

2 In a bowl, mix icing sugar with 1-2 tbsp water and peppermint extract then spread over shortbread base. Leave to set.

3 Melt chocolate in a bowl set over a pan of barely simmering water. Spread over icing and leave in tin to cool. When set, cut into bars.

Makes 10
V F

Time 35 mins
plus cooling

Calories 321
Fibre 1.3g

Salt 0.2g
Sugar 34g

Fat 14g of which
8.7g is saturated

July

M	T	W	T	F	S	S	M	T	W	T	F	S	S
26	27	28	29	30	1	2	3	4	5	6	7	8	9

3 Monday

4 Tuesday

5 Wednesday

6 Thursday

7 Friday

M	T	W	T	F	S	S	M	T	W	T	F	S	S
10	11	12	13	14	15	16	17	18	19	20	21	22	23

July
Week 27

Saturday **8**

Sunday **9**
○ *Full Moon*

Green Pea & Ham Soup

Olive oil 1 tbsp
Onion 1, peeled and chopped
Garlic 1 clove, peeled and finely chopped
Frozen peas 450g (1lb)
Cooked ham 110g (4oz), chopped
Vegetable stock 450ml (¾ pint)
Single cream 150ml pot
Croutons to serve, optional

1 Heat oil in a large saucepan and cook onion and garlic for 5 minutes or until soft.
2 Add peas, 90g (3½ oz) ham and stock and bring to the boil. Reduce heat and simmer for 15 minutes.
3 Remove from the heat, purée with a hand-held blender and season to taste. Serve in warm bowls topped with a generous swirl of cream, remaining ham and croutons, if using.

Serves 3 **Time** 25 mins **Calories** 291 **Salt** 2.5g **Fat** 16g of which
Fibre 9.3g **Sugar** 0g 7.2g is saturated

109

July

	M	T	W	T	F	S	S	M	T	W	T	F	S	S
	3	4	5	6	7	8	9	10	11	12	13	14	15	16

10 Monday

11 Tuesday

12 Wednesday

Bank Holiday, N Ireland

13 Thursday

14 Friday

M	T	W	T	F	S	S	M	T	W	T	F	S	S
17	18	19	20	21	22	23	24	25	26	27	28	29	30

July
Week 28

Saturday **15**

Sunday **16**
(*Last Quarter*

Baked Figs with Honey & Almonds

Figs 4
Ground cinnamon ½ tsp
Honey 2 tbsp
Natural Greek yogurt 4 tbsp
Toasted flaked almonds 1 tbsp

1 Preheat grill to hot. Cut figs into quarters (without cutting all the way through). Open out slightly and place on a baking tray. Sprinkle with cinnamon and drizzle with honey.
2 Place under grill for 3-5 minutes until honey starts to bubble. Serve warm with yogurt and a scattering of almonds.

Serves 2	Time 10 mins	Calories 442	Salt 0.3g	Fat 15g of which
V		Fibre 10g	Sugar 12g	6.4g is saturated

111

July

17 Monday

18 Tuesday

19 Wednesday

20 Thursday

21 Friday

Saturday 22

Sunday 23
● *New Moon*

Garlic Mushroom Tagliatelle

Dried tagliatelle 300g (11oz)
Olive oil 2 tbsp
Red onion 1, peeled and chopped
Garlic 2 cloves, peeled and finely chopped
Portabella mushrooms 250g (9oz), wiped and sliced
Oyster mushrooms 110g (4oz), wiped and sliced
Baby mushrooms 150g (5oz), wiped and halved
Double cream 300ml pot
Chopped parsley and grated cheese to serve, optional

1 Cook tagliatelle according to packet's instructions.
2 Meanwhile, heat oil in a frying pan and cook onion and garlic gently for 5 minutes or until just soft.
3 Add mushrooms and cook, stirring, for 5 minutes or until soft. Add cream and bring to the boil. Simmer for 2-5 minutes until slightly thickened. Season to taste.

Serves 4	Time 20 mins	Calories 706	Salt 0.6g	Fat 47g of which
[V]		Fibre 5.5g	Sugar 0g	26g is saturated

4 Drain tagliatelle and toss with mushroom and cream mixture. Divide between warm pasta bowls and scatter with chopped fresh parsley and grated cheese, if using.

113

July

M	T	W	T	F	S	S	M	T	W	T	F	S	S
17	18	19	20	21	22	23	**24**	**25**	**26**	**27**	**28**	**29**	**30**

24 Monday

25 Tuesday

26 Wednesday

27 Thursday

28 Friday

M	T	W	T	F	S	S	M	T	W	T	F	S	S
31	1	2	3	4	5	6	7	8	9	10	11	12	13

July
Week 30

Saturday 29

Sunday 30
) *First Quarter*

Honey-Roast Spatchcock Chicken

Chicken 1.65-1.8kg (3½-4lb)
Oranges 2 large; 1 quartered, juice of 1
Clear honey 3 tbsp
Sun-dried tomato paste 2 tbsp
Light soy sauce 2 tbsp
Warm bread and crunchy salad to serve, optional

1 Preheat oven to 220°C/200°fan/Gas 7. Place chicken breast-side down on a board and with a sharp knife carefully remove backbone by cutting down each side. Turn over and open out flat. Make a cut in skin between tip of breastbone and each leg and insert top of each legbone into slits. Place in a roasting tin, skin-side up and season well.
2 Mix together orange juice, honey, tomato paste and soy, and spoon over chicken. Place orange quarters in tin and then transfer to oven for 30 minutes.
3 Reduce heat to 180°C/160°fan/Gas 4 and

| Serves 4 | Time 1½ hrs | Calories 893 | Salt 1.8g | Fat 57g of which |
| F | | Fibre 1g | Sugar 9.2g | 16g is saturated |

continue to cook for another 30-45 minutes until chicken is cooked through. Baste frequently and cover with foil if browning too much.

4 Strain pan juices through a sieve and serve with roast chicken accompanied by a crunchy salad and some warm bread, if you like.

115

M	T	W	T	F	S	S	M	T	W	T	F	S	S
24	25	26	27	28	29	30	31	1	2	3	4	5	6

31 Monday

1 Tuesday AUGUST

2 Wednesday

3 Thursday

4 Friday

M	T	W	T	F	S	S	M	T	W	T	F	S	S
7	8	9	10	11	12	13	14	15	16	17	18	19	20

August
Week 31

Saturday 5

Sunday 6

Nacho Chilli Bean & Iceberg Layer

Chilli oil 2 tbsp
White wine vinegar 1 tbsp
Honey 1 tsp
Iceberg lettuce 1, shredded
Mixed beans in spicy sauce 395g can
Ripe avocados 2, diced
Sweetcorn 195g can, drained
Cherry tomatoes 250g pack, halved
Tortilla chips 50g (2oz), lightly crushed

1 Whisk oil, vinegar and honey together and season. Toss half into lettuce and place lettuce in four serving bowls.
2 Warm beans in a small saucepan for 1-2 minutes, then spoon over lettuce.
3 Mix together avocado, sweetcorn and tomatoes and toss in remaining dressing. Spoon over beans, sprinkle with tortilla chips and serve.

Serves 4
V
Time 15 mins
Calories 309
Fibre 7g
Salt 0.9g
Sugar 1.5g
Fat 19g of which 2.3g is saturated

August

M	T	W	T	F	S	S	M	T	W	T	F	S	S
31	1	2	3	4	5	6	7	8	9	10	11	12	13

7 Monday

○ *Full Moon*
Bank Holiday, Scotland

8 Tuesday

9 Wednesday

10 Thursday

11 Friday

M	T	W	T	F	S	S	M	T	W	T	F	S	S
14	15	16	17	18	19	20	21	22	23	24	25	26	27

August
Week 32

Saturday **12**

Sunday **13**

Raspberry & Macadamia Cake

Macadamia nuts 125g (4½oz)
Light brown sugar 50g (2oz)
Caster sugar 110g (4oz)
Unsalted butter 175g (6oz), softened
Eggs 2
Almond extract a few drops
Self-raising flour 150g (5oz), sifted
Raspberries 200g (7oz)
Milk 2 tbsp
Demerara sugar 1 heaped tbsp

1 Preheat oven to 180°C/160°fan/Gas 4. Grease and line a 900g (2lb) loaf tin.
2 Whizz macadamia nuts in a food processor until finely ground.
3 Beat together brown sugar, caster sugar and butter until light and fluffy. Gradually beat in eggs and almond extract then fold in flour and nuts. When combined, gently fold in raspberries and milk.
4 Pour cake mixture into prepared tin and bake for 45 minutes (you may need to cover with foil). Remove from oven, scatter with demerara sugar and return to oven for 5 minutes or until a skewer comes out clean. Leave to cool in tin.

Slices 10	Time 1½ hrs	Calories 368	Salt 0.3g	Fat 25g of which
V F		Fibre 2.1g	Sugar 20g	11g is saturated

August

M	T	W	T	F	S	S	M	T	W	T	F	S	S
7	8	9	10	11	12	13	**14**	**15**	**16**	**17**	**18**	**19**	**20**

---

14 Monday

---

15 Tuesday

☾ *Last Quarter*

---

16 Wednesday

---

17 Thursday

---

18 Friday

M	T	W	T	F	S	S	M	T	W	T	F	S	S
21	22	23	24	25	26	27	28	29	30	31	1	2	3

August
Week 33

Saturday 19

Sunday 20

Spanish Tapas Platter

Potatoes 275g (10oz), peeled and thinly sliced
Chorizo 75g (3oz), chopped
Red onion 1, peeled and thinly sliced
Garlic 2 cloves, peeled and finely chopped
Paprika 1½ tsp
Eggs 6, beaten
Shelled raw prawns 180g/200g pack
Butter 25g (1oz)
Serrano ham and/or Salchichon 175g (6oz)
Manchego cheese 75g (3oz), cubed
Olives 110g (4oz)
Chargrilled peppers and/or tomatoes 175g (6oz), drained

Serves 4	Time 40 mins	Calories 533	Salt 5.2g	Fat 33g of which
		Fibre 4.8g	Sugar 0g	13.9g is saturated

1 Place potatoes in a saucepan, cover with water and bring to the boil. Cook for 5-7 minutes until just tender. Drain.
2 In a frying pan fry chorizo with onion and 1 clove garlic for 5 minutes. Add potato. Mix 1 tsp paprika with eggs and season then pour onto potato. Cook for 10-15 minutes until just set.
3 Fry prawns in butter with remaining garlic for 4 minutes or until cooked. Dust with paprika.
4 Brown omelette under grill then cut into quarters. Place onto a board and serve with prawns and all remaining ingredients.

121

August

21 Monday
● *New Moon*

London Pk.

David, Paul & Mark
for day

22 Tuesday

23 Wednesday

24 Thursday

Paul, Mark & David
London for day

25 Friday

Mark & David for day

M	T	W	T	F	S	S	M	T	W	T	F	S	S
28	29	30	31	1	2	3	4	5	6	7	8	9	10

August
Week 34

Saturday **26**

Sunday **27**

Mackerel Fish Cakes

Potatoes 2 (approx. 425g/15oz), peeled and cut into chunks
Milk 2-3 tbsp
Butter 50g (2oz), melted
Peppered smoked mackerel fillets 350g (12oz), flaked
Chopped parsley 1 tbsp
Horseradish sauce 2 tbsp
Egg 1, beaten
Fresh white breadcrumbs 50g (2oz)
Sunflower oil 2 tbsp
Light mayonnaise 4 tbsp
Vegetables to serve, optional

1 Cook potatoes in lightly salted boiling water for 12-15 minutes until tender.
2 Drain potatoes and mash with milk and 25g (1oz) butter. Stir in mackerel, parsley and 1 tbsp horseradish. Divide mixture into 8 and mould each into a fish cake. Dip each in egg and coat in breadcrumbs.
3 Heat remaining butter and oil in a large frying pan and gently cook fish cakes for 4-5 minutes on each side until golden.
4 Stir remaining horseradish into mayonnaise.
5 Serve fish cakes immediately with horseradish mayonnaise and steamed green vegetables.

Serves 4	**Time** 40 mins	**Calories** 614	**Salt** 2.2g	**Fat** 43g of which
F		**Fibre** 2.4g	**Sugar** 0g	12.4g is saturated

August

M	T	W	T	F	S	S	M	T	W	T	F	S	S
21	22	23	24	25	26	27	**28**	**29**	**30**	**31**	**1**	**2**	**3**

28 Monday

Bank Holiday, England, Wales and N Ireland

29 Tuesday

) *First Quarter*

30 Wednesday

31 Thursday

1 Friday SEPTEMBER

Abigail for week-end ?

M	T	W	T	F	S	S	M	T	W	T	F	S	S
4	5	6	7	8	9	10	11	12	13	14	15	16	17

September
Week 35

Saturday **2**

Sunday **3**

Steak Topped with Mushrooms

Butter 25g (1oz)
Mushrooms 75g (3oz), wiped and finely sliced
White wine 2 tbsp
Soft cheese with garlic and herbs 2 tbsp
Parmesan 1 tbsp
Lean picanha, sirloin, rump or rib-eye steaks 2, seasoned
Rapeseed or sunflower oil 1 tbsp
Potato wedges and salad to serve, optional

1 Heat butter in a frying pan suitable for use under the grill and cook mushrooms for 2-3 minutes until soft. Add wine and simmer until evaporated. Transfer to a bowl, add cheeses and stir together. Preheat grill.
2 Heat frying pan until hot, brush steaks with oil and add to pan. Cook according to your preference (for a 2cm/¾in thick steak allow: rare 2½ minutes, medium 4 minutes, well-done 6 minutes each side).

Serves 2	Time 15 mins	Calories 485	Salt 1.9g	Fat 30g of which
		Fibre 0.3g	Sugar 0g	15g is saturated

3 Spoon cheese and mushroom topping onto each steak. Place under grill for 1-2 minutes until topping is golden brown. Serve immediately with potato wedges and a fresh leafy salad, if using.

125

September

4 Monday

5 Tuesday

6 Wednesday

○ *Full Moon*

7 Thursday

8 Friday

M	T	W	T	F	S	S	M	T	W	T	F	S	S
11	12	13	14	15	16	17	18	19	20	21	22	23	24

September
Week 36

Saturday 9

Aleso a Co to Croatia

Sunday 10

Roasted Spicy Squash Salad

Butternut squash 1kg (2lb 4oz), peeled, deseeded and cut into 2cm (¾in) cubes
Olive oil 4 tbsp
Crushed chilli flakes 1 tsp
Paprika 1 tsp
Pumpkin seeds 50g (2oz)
Dark soy sauce 3 tbsp
White wine vinegar 2 tbsp
Honey 1 tbsp
Watercress, rocket & spinach salad 140g bag

1 Preheat oven to 200°C/180°fan/Gas 6. Place squash in a large roasting tin, toss in 2 tbsp oil, chilli flakes, paprika and pumpkin seeds. Season and roast for 20 minutes or until tender.
2 Whisk together soy sauce, vinegar, honey and remaining oil. Toss dressing into salad and then gently mix in warm squash and seeds. Serve immediately.

Serves 4	Time 30 mins	Calories 294	Salt 2.1g	Fat 17g of which
V		Fibre 6.9g	Sugar 4.5g	2.6g is saturated

September

11 Monday

12 Tuesday

13 Wednesday

☾ *Last Quarter*

14 Thursday

15 Friday

M	T	W	T	F	S	S	M	T	W	T	F	S	S
18	19	20	21	22	23	24	25	26	27	28	29	30	1

September
Week 37

Saturday 16

Sunday 17

Blackberry & Bay Jelly

Blackberries 1kg (2lb 4oz)
Cooking apples 450g (1lb),
peeled, cored and chopped
Bay leaves 4, torn
Jam sugar 1-1.5kg (2-3lb)
Jars 4-6, sterilised
Cheese or cold meat to serve,
optional

1 Place fruit and bay leaves into a preserving pan with 600ml (1 pint) water. Cover and cook gently for 30 minutes or until soft and very mushy.
2 Strain pulp through a nylon sieve set over a bowl. Measure resulting liquid and return it to pan, adding 500g (1lb 2oz) of sugar for each 500ml (18fl oz) of liquor. Stir over a low heat until sugar has dissolved, then bring mixture to the boil. Reduce to a simmer, stirring regularly, for 50-70 minutes.
3 Test for set by placing a tsp of mixture onto a cold saucer. If surface wrinkles when touched, it's ready. As soon as it is ready,

Makes 1kg	**Time** 1¾ hrs	**Calories** 67	**Salt** 0g	**Fat** 0g of which
(2lb 4oz)	V Per tbsp:	**Fibre** 0.8g	**Sugar** 15g	0g is saturated

skim off any scum from the top, pour into jars, and cover with waxed discs. Leave until cold,

then seal and store in a cool, dark place until required. Best served with cheese or cold meat.

September

M	T	W	T	F	S	S	M	T	W	T	F	S	S
11	12	13	14	15	16	17	**18**	**19**	**20**	**21**	**22**	**23**	**24**

---

18 Monday

---

19 Tuesday

---

20 Wednesday

● *New Moon*

---

21 Thursday

---

22 Friday

Autumnal equinox
Autumn begins

M	T	W	T	F	S	S	M	T	W	T	F	S	S
25	26	27	28	29	30	1	2	3	4	5	6	7	8

September
Week 38

Saturday 23

Sunday 24

Easy Chicken Curry

Butter 25g (1oz)
Onion 1, peeled and chopped
Dessert apple 1, peeled, cored and chopped
Butternut squash 150g (5oz), peeled and diced
Curry paste 1 tbsp
Plain flour 1 tbsp
Ground ginger ½ tsp
Ground cinnamon ½ tsp
Milk 225ml (8fl oz)
Mango chutney 1 tbsp
Cooked chicken 175-225g (6-8oz), cut into chunks
Cooked basmati rice, naan bread and flaked almonds to serve, optional

1 Melt butter in a saucepan and add onion, apple, squash and curry paste. Cover and cook on a low heat for 5 minutes.
2 Add flour, ginger and cinnamon and cook for 1 minute, stirring.
3 Pour milk into pan, then add mango chutney and cooked chicken. Bring to the boil,
stirring, then reduce the heat, cover with a lid and simmer gently for 20 minutes.
4 Serve curry on a bed of rice sprinkled with almonds and with naan bread, if using.

Serves 2	Time 30 mins	Calories 417	Salt 1.1g	Fat 17g of which
F		Fibre 4.2g	Sugar 9.7g	8.5g is saturated

131

September

M	T	W	T	F	S	S	M	T	W	T	F	S	S
18	19	20	21	22	23	24	**25**	**26**	**27**	**28**	**29**	**30**	1

25 Monday

Don't forget to order your 2018 Dairy Diary. Use the order form on page 170 or order online.
If you don't have a milkman, call 0845 0948 128 or visit www.dairydiary.co.uk

26 Tuesday

27 Wednesday

28 Thursday

⟩ *First Quarter*

29 Friday

M	T	W	T	F	S	S	M	T	W	T	F	S	S
2	3	4	5	6	7	8	9	10	11	12	13	14	15

September
Week 39

Saturday 30

OCTOBER Sunday 1

Pear & Cinnamon Crumbles

Pears 4, peeled, cored and chopped
Caster sugar 1 tbsp
Butter 110g (4oz)
Demerara sugar 110g (4oz)
Ground almonds 110g (4oz)
Plain flour 110g (4oz)
Ground cinnamon 1 tsp
Flaked almonds 2 tbsp

1 Preheat oven to 190°C/170°fan/Gas 5. Place pears and caster sugar in a saucepan with 2 tbsp water. Cook gently for 5-8 minutes, until soft.
2 Spoon pears into 4 ovenproof ramekins using a slotted spoon. Tip all remaining ingredients except almonds into a food processor and pulse several times until mixture resembles breadcrumbs. Sprinkle crumble mixture over pears and top with flaked almonds.
3 Bake for 20 minutes or until topping is golden.

Serves 4
V F
Time 40 mins
Calories 657
Fibre 7.2g
Salt 0.4g
Sugar 35g
Fat 41g of which
16g is saturated

133

October

2 Monday

3 Tuesday

4 Wednesday

5 Thursday

○ *Full Moon*

6 Friday

M	T	W	T	F	S	S	M	T	W	T	F	S	S
9	10	11	12	13	14	15	16	17	18	19	20	21	22

October
Week 40

Saturday 7

Sunday 8

Celebrate 35 Years of the Dairy Diary & Win a Year of Flowers!

2017 heralds the 35th anniversary of the ever-popular Dairy Diary and to celebrate we're giving you the chance to win a year of flowers. Appleyard London is kindly offering one very lucky reader a bouquet of their choice (each up to the value of £40) delivered to an address of their choice every month.

Appleyard London offer a huge variety of bouquets and gifts to ensure the recipient is left feeling incredibly special. So whether you want to send flowers to a loved one or treat yourself visit www.appleyardflowers.com.

To enter the prize draw visit
www.dairydiary.co.uk/win2017

If you don't have access to the internet, you can enter by sending your name and address to:

Appleyard Competition, Eaglemoss Ltd, Electra House, Electra Way, Crewe, CW1 6GL

The closing date is 30th November 2017.

You can order your **2018 Dairy Diary** via your **milkman** (see p170), online at **www.dairydiary.co.uk** or by calling **0845 0948 128**.

135

October

9 Monday

10 Tuesday

11 Wednesday

12 Thursday

☾ *Last Quarter*

13 Friday

M	T	W	T	F	S	S	M	T	W	T	F	S	S
16	17	18	19	20	21	22	23	24	25	26	27	28	29

October
Week 41

Saturday **14**

Sunday **15**

Oatie Melting Moments

Butter 110g (4oz), softened
Caster sugar 75g (3oz)
Egg yolk 1
Vanilla extract a few drops
Self-raising flour 150g (5oz)
Rolled oats 25g (1oz)

1 Preheat oven to
190°C/170°fan/Gas 5 and grease
two baking sheets.
2 Cream together butter and
sugar until pale and fluffy, then
beat in egg yolk and vanilla.
3 Stir in flour to give a soft
dough, knead until smooth, then
divide into 24 portions. Form
each portion into a ball, then
gently roll in oats.
4 Place on baking sheets and
bake for 15-20 minutes until
golden. Cool slightly before
transferring to a wire rack to
cool completely.

Makes 24   **Time** 40 mins   **Calories** 74   **Salt** 0.1g   **Fat** 4.2g of which
V F   **Fibre** 0.4g   **Sugar** 3.1g   2.5g is saturated

137

October

16 Monday

17 Tuesday

18 Wednesday

19 Thursday

● *New Moon*

20 Friday

M	T	W	T	F	S	S	M	T	W	T	F	S	S
23	24	25	26	27	28	29	30	31	1	2	3	4	5

October
Week 42

Saturday 21

Sunday 22

Beetroot & Feta Baked Potatoes

Baking potatoes 2, scrubbed and pricked
Feta cheese 50g (2oz), crumbled
Cooked beetroot 150g (5oz), chopped
Orange or red pepper ½, deseeded and diced
Cherry tomatoes 4, quartered
Spring onions 2, sliced
Rocket leaves to serve

1 Preheat oven to 200°C/180°fan/Gas 6. Bake potatoes for 1-1½ hours until cooked through.
2 Cut a large cross in the top of each potato and add feta. Sprinkle with freshly ground black pepper and then pile beetroot, pepper, tomatoes and onions on top. Top with a few leaves and serve.

Serves 2
[V]
Time 1½ hrs
Calories 323
Fibre 8g
Salt 1.2g
Sugar 0g
Fat 5.9g of which 3.5g is saturated

139

October

M	T	W	T	F	S	S	M	T	W	T	F	S	S
16	17	18	19	20	21	22	**23**	**24**	**25**	**26**	**27**	**28**	**29**

23 Monday

24 Tuesday

25 Wednesday

26 Thursday

27 Friday

) *First Quarter*

M	T	W	T	F	S	S	M	T	W	T	F	S	S
30	31	1	2	3	4	5	6	7	8	9	10	11	12

October
Week 43

Saturday 28
Don't forget to put your clocks back 1 hour tonight

Sunday 29
British Summer Time ends

Parsnip & Apple Soup

Butter 50g (2oz)
Dessert apple 1, peeled, cored and sliced
Parsnips 680g (1½lb), peeled and sliced
Cooking apple 1, peeled, cored and sliced
Vegetable stock 1.25 litres (2 pints)
Sage leaves 4, plus extra to garnish
Whole cloves 2
Single cream 150ml pot

1 Melt half the butter in a large saucepan and sauté dessert apple until browned. Set aside.
2 Melt remaining butter and add parsnips and cooking apple. Cover and cook gently for 10 minutes.
3 Pour stock into saucepan, add sage leaves and cloves and bring to the boil. Cover and simmer for 30 minutes or until parsnips are soft.
4 Take pan off the heat, remove sage leaves and cloves, then purée with a hand-held blender and season to taste. Stir in cream and reheat gently until hot but not boiling. Serve immediately garnished with sage and reserved apple slices.

Serves 6	**Time** 55 mins	**Calories** 203	**Salt** 1.9g	**Fat** 14g of which
V F		**Fibre** 7.5g	**Sugar** 0g	7.6g is saturated

141

October

30 Monday

31 Tuesday

Halloween

1 Wednesday NOVEMBER

2 Thursday

3 Friday

M	T	W	T	F	S	S	M	T	W	T	F	S	S
6	7	8	9	10	11	12	13	14	15	16	17	18	19

November
Week 44

Saturday 4
○ *Full Moon*

Sunday 5
Bonfire Night

Pumpkin Streusel Muffins

Butter 150g (5oz)
Plain flour 300g (11oz)
Baking powder 2 tsp
Ground cinnamon 1 tsp
Caster sugar 110g (4oz)
Eggs 2 large, beaten
Milk 200ml (7fl oz)
Pumpkin 275g (10oz), peeled, deseeded and grated
Raisins 75g (3oz)
Self-raising flour 50g (2oz)
Demerara sugar 50g (2oz)

1 Preheat oven to 190°C/170°fan/Gas 5 and place 12 muffin cases in a muffin tin. Melt 110g (4oz) butter.
2 In a large mixing bowl sift plain flour, baking powder and cinnamon, then stir in caster sugar. Make a well in centre and pour in eggs, milk and melted butter. Stir until just combined, then fold in pumpkin and raisins. Spoon into muffin cases.
3 In a separate bowl rub remaining butter into self-raising flour then stir in demerara sugar.

Makes 12	**Time** 1¼ hrs	**Calories** 288	**Salt** 0.5g	**Fat** 12g of which
V F		**Fibre** 1.7g	**Sugar** 16g	7.1g is saturated

Sprinkle over batter in cases then bake for 30-40 minutes until risen and golden.

4 Leave in muffin tin for 5 minutes then cool on a wire rack. Serve warm or cold.

November

M	T	W	T	F	S	S	M	T	W	T	F	S	S
30	31	1	2	3	4	5	6	7	8	9	10	11	12

6 Monday

7 Tuesday

8 Wednesday

9 Thursday

10 Friday

☾ *Last Quarter*

M	T	W	T	F	S	S	M	T	W	T	F	S	S
13	14	15	16	17	18	19	20	21	22	23	24	25	26

November
Week 45

Saturday 11

Sunday 12
Remembrance Sunday

Creamy Pasta with Sausages

Red onions 2, peeled and sliced
Red wine vinegar 2 tbsp
Pasta shapes 350g (12oz)
Thick pork sausages 450g (1lb)
Butter 15g (½oz)
Olive oil 1 tbsp
Clear honey 1 tbsp
Double cream 150ml (¼ pint)
Wholegrain mustard 2 tbsp

1 Toss onions in vinegar and leave to stand for 5 minutes.
2 Cook pasta shapes and sausages according to each packet's instructions.
3 Meanwhile, melt butter with olive oil and fry onions with red wine vinegar for 5 minutes until just softened. Add honey and cook for a further 5 minutes, stirring frequently.
4 Gently heat cream with mustard for 2-3 minutes until hot. Drain pasta and cut sausages into chunks. Mix with onions and cream. Spoon into pasta bowls and sprinkle with freshly ground black pepper.

Serves 4	Time 25 mins	Calories 937	Salt 1.3g	Fat 56g of which
		Fibre 9.3g	Sugar 4.5g	25g is saturated

November

13 Monday

14 Tuesday

Birthday of the Prince of Wales

15 Wednesday

16 Thursday

17 Friday

M	T	W	T	F	S	S	M	T	W	T	F	S	S
20	21	22	23	24	25	26	27	28	29	30	1	2	3

November
Week 46

Saturday 18

● *New Moon*

Sunday 19

Ice Cream with Pistachio & Cranberry Brittle

Unsalted pistachio nut kernels
50g (2oz)
Dried cranberries 25g (1oz)
Caster sugar 110g (4oz)
Butter 50g (2oz)
Luxury vanilla ice cream
Maple syrup or fruit coulis to
serve, optional

1 Line a small baking tray or
dish (approx. 22cm x 16cm/9in x
6in) with non-stick baking paper
and scatter with pistachio nuts
and cranberries.
2 Put sugar, butter, ¼ tsp salt
and 4 tbsp water into a saucepan
and heat gently, stirring, until
butter has melted and sugar has
dissolved. Then bring to the boil
and boil, stirring, for 5-8 minutes
until it starts to turn toffee-
coloured. Immediately pour over
fruit and nuts and leave until
cold. Break into small pieces.
3 Spoon 2-3 scoops ice cream
into sundae glasses, drizzle with
syrup or coulis, if using, and top
with brittle. Serve immediately.

Serves 4-6	Time 20 mins	Calories 239	Salt 0.2g	Fat 14g of which
V	plus cooling	Fibre 1.7g	Sugar 25g	6.5g is saturated

November

20 Monday

21 Tuesday

22 Wednesday

23 Thursday

24 Friday

M	T	W	T	F	S	S	M	T	W	T	F	S	S
27	28	29	30	1	2	3	4	5	6	7	8	9	10

November
Week 47

Saturday **25**

Sunday **26**
⟩ *First Quarter*

Sticky Ribs with Baked Potatoes

Pork ribs pack of 6
Sunflower oil 1 tbsp
Tomato ketchup 2 tbsp
Paprika 1 tsp
Ground cumin ½ tsp
Chilli powder ¼ tsp
Baking potatoes 2, scrubbed
and pricked
Cooked corn on the cob 2, to
serve, optional

1 Preheat oven to
200°C/180°fan/Gas 6 and line
a small roasting tin with foil.
2 Place ribs in tin and add a
splash of water. Mix oil, ketchup,
paprika, cumin and chilli with
salt and pepper and spoon over
ribs. Place on shelf just above
the centre of the oven for
1¼-1½ hours. Bake potatoes
alongside ribs. Turn ribs halfway
through cooking and brush with
pan juices.
3 Serve cooked ribs and
potatoes, with corn on the cob
if you like.

Serves 2	**Time** 1½ hrs	**Calories** 756	**Salt** 0.9g	**Fat** 40g of which
		Fibre 6.1g	**Sugar** 2.5g	14g is saturated

November

27 Monday

28 Tuesday

29 Wednesday

30 Thursday

St Andrew's Day

1 Friday DECEMBER

M	T	W	T	F	S	S	M	T	W	T	F	S	S
4	5	6	7	8	9	10	11	12	13	14	15	16	17

December
Week 48

Saturday 2

Sunday 3
○ *Full Moon*
First Sunday in Advent

Chocolate & Hazelnut Tart

Eggs 2 plus 1 yolk
Icing sugar 2 tsp
Cocoa powder 1 tbsp plus extra for sifting
Plain flour 110g (4oz)
Butter 65g (2½oz), cubed
70% cocoa dark chocolate 200g (7oz), broken into pieces
Milk 125ml (4fl oz)
Double cream 200ml (7fl oz)
Hazelnuts 150g (5oz), chopped
Clotted or whipped double cream to serve

1 Mix 1 egg yolk, icing sugar, cocoa powder, flour, a pinch of salt and butter together in a food processor until combined. Press together with your hands then wrap in a polythene bag and chill for 30 minutes.
2 Preheat oven to 170°C/ 150°fan/Gas 3. Press dough into base and sides of a 20cm (8in) round loose-based tin. Prick base, place on a baking tray and bake for 30 minutes or until crisp.

Serves 10	Time 1 hour	Calories 424	Salt 0.1g	Fat 33g of which
V F	plus chilling	Fibre 2.3g	Sugar 16g	14g is saturated

3 Reduce oven to 140°C/ 120°fan/Gas 1. In a pan heat milk and cream until boiling then remove from heat and whisk in chocolate then 2 eggs.

4 Scatter nuts onto pastry, fill with chocolate and bake for 20-30 minutes or until just set. Cool, then chill, sift with cocoa, if you like, and serve with cream.

151

December

M	T	W	T	F	S	S	M	T	W	T	F	S	S
27	28	29	30	1	2	3	4	5	6	7	8	9	10

4 Monday

5 Tuesday

6 Wednesday

7 Thursday

8 Friday

M	T	W	T	F	S	S	M	T	W	T	F	S	S
11	12	13	14	15	16	17	18	19	20	21	22	23	24

December
Week 49

Saturday **9**

Sunday **10**
☾ *Last Quarter*

Layered Berry Breakfast Pots

Muesli 75g (3oz)
Goji berries 2 tbsp
Freshly squeezed orange juice 100ml (3½fl oz)
Coconut or honey flavoured Greek-style yogurt 500g tub
Strawberries 350g (12oz), hulled and mashed, plus extra slices to garnish
Chia seeds 1 tbsp
Blackberries 110g (4oz)
Few extra strawberries, hulled, sliced

1 Mix muesli, goji berries and orange juice together then spoon half the mixture into the base of 4 x 370g (12½oz) clip-top or screw-top jam jars. Top with a layer of yogurt.
2 Mix strawberries with seeds and spoon over yogurt.
3 Cover with most of remaining muesli then the yogurt. Sprinkle with blackberries, a few strawberry slices and the rest of the muesli. Clip or screw on the lids and chill until ready to serve.

Serves 4	Time 15 mins	Calories 308	Salt 1.6g	Fat 16g of which
		Fibre 7.1g	Sugar 8g	9g is saturated

December

11 Monday

12 Tuesday

13 Wednesday

14 Thursday

15 Friday

M	T	W	T	F	S	S	M	T	W	T	F	S	S
18	19	20	21	22	23	24	25	26	27	28	29	30	31

December
Week 50

Saturday **16**

Sunday **17**

Mincemeat Cakes

Butter 125g (4½oz)
Caster sugar 125g (4½oz)
Eggs 2 large, beaten
Self-raising flour 200g (7oz)
Mincemeat 312g jar
Icing sugar 225g (8oz) plus a little extra, sifted
Green and red ready-to-roll icing

1 Preheat oven to 160°C/140°fan/Gas 3. Grease and base line a 12 hole muffin tin.
2 In a large bowl beat together butter, caster sugar, eggs and flour. Stir in mincemeat then spoon into tin. Bake for 25-30 minutes or until golden and firm.
3 Leave to cool in tin then loosen edges with a palette knife and invert tin onto a wire rack. Leave cakes upside down.
4 Mix icing sugar with 2-2½ tbsp water. Spoon over cakes allowing to run down sides a little. Cut out holly leaves and berries from icing and use to decorate. Sift with icing sugar.

Makes 12	**Time** 1 hr	**Calories** 349	**Salt** 0.4g	**Fat** 11g of which
F	plus cooling	**Fibre** 1.1g	**Sugar** 34g	5.7g is saturated

December

M	T	W	T	F	S	S	M	T	W	T	F	S	S
11	12	13	14	15	16	17	**18**	**19**	**20**	**21**	**22**	**23**	**24**

18 Monday
● *New Moon*

19 Tuesday

20 Wednesday

21 Thursday
Winter solstice
Winter begins

22 Friday

M	T	W	T	F	S	S	M	T	W	T	F	S	S
25	26	27	28	29	30	31	1	2	3	4	5	6	7

December
Week 51

Saturday 23

Sunday 24

Gingerbread Latte Trifles

Espresso ground coffee 2 tbsp
Trifle sponges 8 (approx. 200g/7oz), each cut into 3
Custard 500g carton
Double cream 300ml pot
Gingerbread syrup 1 tbsp
Dark chocolate with ginger 50g (2oz), finely chopped

1 Spoon coffee into a cafetière and add 250ml (9fl oz) hot, not boiling, water. Stir and leave to brew for 3 minutes. Plunge, then leave to cool.
2 Place sponges in the base of six trifle bowls. Spoon over coffee then top with custard.
3 Whisk cream with gingerbread syrup until softly whipped. Spoon on top of custard then sprinkle with chocolate. Cover and chill for at least 2 hours or until ready to serve.

Serves 6
[V]
Time 30 mins plus chilling
Calories 535
Fibre 0.6g
Salt 0.5g
Sugar 24g
Fat 40g of which 25g is saturated

157

December

25 Monday

Christmas Day
Bank Holiday, UK

26 Tuesday

) *First Quarter*
Boxing Day
Bank Holiday, UK

27 Wednesday

28 Thursday

29 Friday

M	T	W	T	F	S	S	M	T	W	T	F	S	S
1	2	3	4	5	6	7	8	9	10	11	12	13	14

December
Week 52

Saturday 30

Sunday 31
New Year's Eve

Mixed Berries Mulled Wine

Orange 1 large, finely grated zest and juice
Caster sugar 125g (4½oz)
Cloves 6
Cinnamon sticks 2
Grated nutmeg ¼ tsp
Vanilla pod 1, halved lengthways
Red wine 2 bottles
Brandy 3 tbsp
Frozen mixed berries 200g (7oz)

1 Place orange zest and juice in a large saucepan with sugar, spices and vanilla pod. Add just enough red wine to cover ingredients. Heat gently, stirring, until sugar has dissolved. Bring to the boil and boil rapidly for 8 minutes or until wine has reduced and become syrupy.
2 Pour in remaining wine, brandy and berries. Heat gently for 2 minutes, but do not boil. Serve in heatproof glasses.

Serves 8-10　**Time** 20 mins　**Calories** 182　**Salt** 0g　**Fat** 0.2g of which
V　　　　　　　　　　　　　　　**Fibre** 0.5g　**Sugar** 14g　0.1g is saturated

159

January

1 Monday JANUARY 2018

New Year's Day
Bank Holiday, UK

2 Tuesday

○ *Full Moon*
Bank Holiday, Scotland

3 Wednesday

4 Thursday

5 Friday

Notes

Notes

Notes

Notes

Notes

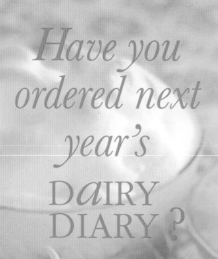

Have you ordered next year's Dairy Diary?

Three ways to order:

FROM YOUR MILKMAN
Use the **order form on p170**, or, if you usually order via your dairy's website, order online.

TELEPHONE
If you do not have a milkman, ring **0845 0948 128**, or **01425 463390**. Place your order over the phone and your diary will be posted to you.

ONLINE
Visit **dairydiary.co.uk**
See full details of the 2018 Dairy Diary and other products.

FOR MORE RECIPES, COMPETITIONS, FEATURES AND NEWS:
Visit us at **dairydiary.co.uk**
Read our blog **dairydiarychat.co.uk**
Follow us on Twitter **@thedairydiary**
Check our Dairy Diary page on **Facebook**

Reserve YOUR COPY OF THE

Dairy DIARY 2018

To order your copy of the 2018 Dairy Diary, please fill in the order form overleaf and leave it out for your milkman with your empties from September 2017.

If you usually order via your dairy's website, order online.

Dairy Diary 2018

Order FORM

MILKMAN PLEASE LEAVE ME:

☐ copies of the 2018 Dairy Diary

☐ copies of the 2018 Dairy Diary Set

Name ....

Address...

....

....

....

....

Postcode...

Thank you
Leave out for your milkman from
September 2017 onwards

Recipe INDEX

RECIPE NOTES

■ Nutritional information has been calculated by portion or item. Where there are portion variations, e.g. serves 6-8, the analysis given is based on the larger number.
■ Spoon measures are level unless otherwise stated.
■ Eggs are large unless otherwise stated.

V Suitable for vegetarians, provided a suitable cheese or yogurt is used.
F Suitable for freezing.

SAFETY NOTES

■ Recipes using nuts or nut products are not suitable for young children or those with a nut allergy.
■ Certain at-risk groups, such as pregnant women, babies and sick or elderly people should not eat raw or lightly cooked eggs.

DESSERTS

CAKES & BAKES

MISCELLANEOUS

Year planner 2018

JANUARY		FEBRUARY	MARCH	
1 Mon	BANK HOLIDAY	1 Thu	1 Thu	
2 Tue	BANK HOLIDAY SCOTLAND	2 Fri	2 Fri	
3 Wed		3 Sat	3 Sat	
4 Thu		4 Sun	4 Sun	
5 Fri		5 Mon	5 Mon	
6 Sat		6 Tue	6 Tue	
7 Sun		7 Wed	7 Wed	
8 Mon		8 Thu	8 Thu	
9 Tue		9 Fri	9 Fri	
10 Wed		10 Sat	10 Sat	
11 Thu		11 Sun	11 Sun	
12 Fri		12 Mon	12 Mon	
13 Sat		13 Tue	13 Tue	
14 Sun		14 Wed	14 Wed	
15 Mon		15 Thu	15 Thu	
16 Tue		16 Fri	16 Fri	
17 Wed		17 Sat	17 Sat	
18 Thu		18 Sun	18 Sun	
19 Fri		19 Mon	19 Mon	BANK HOLIDAY N IRELAND
20 Sat		20 Tue	20 Tue	
21 Sun		21 Wed	21 Wed	
22 Mon		22 Thu	22 Thu	
23 Tue		23 Fri	23 Fri	
24 Wed		24 Sat	24 Sat	
25 Thu		25 Sun	25 Sun	
26 Fri		26 Mon	26 Mon	
27 Sat		27 Tue	27 Tue	
28 Sun		28 Wed	28 Wed	
29 Mon			29 Thu	
30 Tue			30 Fri	BANK HOLIDAY
31 Wed			31 Sat	

APRIL		MAY		JUNE	
1	Sun	1	Tue	1	Fri
2	Mon — BANK HOLIDAY	2	Wed	2	Sat
3	Tue	3	Thu	3	Sun
4	Wed	4	Fri	4	Mon
5	Thu	5	Sat	5	Tue
6	Fri	6	Sun	6	Wed
7	Sat	7	Mon — BANK HOLIDAY	7	Thu
8	Sun	8	Tue	8	Fri
9	Mon	9	Wed	9	Sat
10	Tue	10	Thu	10	Sun
11	Wed	11	Fri	11	Mon
12	Thu	12	Sat	12	Tue
13	Fri	13	Sun	13	Wed
14	Sat	14	Mon	14	Thu
15	Sun	15	Tue	15	Fri
16	Mon	16	Wed	16	Sat
17	Tue	17	Thu	17	Sun
18	Wed	18	Fri	18	Mon
19	Thu	19	Sat	19	Tue
20	Fri	20	Sun	20	Wed
21	Sat	21	Mon	21	Thu
22	Sun	22	Tue	22	Fri
23	Mon	23	Wed	23	Sat
24	Tue	24	Thu	24	Sun
25	Wed	25	Fri	25	Mon
26	Thu	26	Sat	26	Tue
27	Fri	27	Sun	27	Wed
28	Sat	28	Mon — BANK HOLIDAY	28	Thu
29	Sun	29	Tue	29	Fri
30	Mon	30	Wed	30	Sat
		31	Thu		

Year planner 2018

JULY		AUGUST		SEPTEMBER	
1	Sun	1	Wed	1	Sat
2	Mon	2	Thu	2	Sun
3	Tue	3	Fri	3	Mon
4	Wed	4	Sat	4	Tue
5	Thu	5	Sun	5	Wed
6	Fri	6	Mon BANK HOLIDAY SCOTLAND	6	Thu
7	Sat	7	Tue	7	Fri
8	Sun	8	Wed	8	Sat
9	Mon	9	Thu	9	Sun
10	Tue	10	Fri	10	Mon
11	Wed	11	Sat	11	Tue
12	Thu BANK HOLIDAY N IRELAND	12	Sun	12	Wed
13	Fri	13	Mon	13	Thu
14	Sat	14	Tue	14	Fri
15	Sun	15	Wed	15	Sat
16	Mon	16	Thu	16	Sun
17	Tue	17	Fri	17	Mon
18	Wed	18	Sat	18	Tue
19	Thu	19	Sun	19	Wed
20	Fri	20	Mon	20	Thu
21	Sat	21	Tue	21	Fri
22	Sun	22	Wed	22	Sat
23	Mon	23	Thu	23	Sun
24	Tue	24	Fri	24	Mon
25	Wed	25	Sat	25	Tue
26	Thu	26	Sun	26	Wed
27	Fri	27	Mon BANK HOLIDAY	27	Thu
28	Sat	28	Tue	28	Fri
29	Sun	29	Wed	29	Sat
30	Mon	30	Thu	30	Sun
31	Tue	31	Fri		

OCTOBER	NOVEMBER	DECEMBER
1 Mon	1 Thu	1 **Sat**
2 Tue	2 Fri	2 **Sun**
3 Wed	3 **Sat**	3 Mon
4 Thu	4 **Sun**	4 Tue
5 Fri	5 Mon	5 Wed
6 **Sat**	6 Tue	6 Thu
7 **Sun**	7 Wed	7 Fri
8 Mon	8 Thu	8 **Sat**
9 Tue	9 Fri	9 **Sun**
10 Wed	10 **Sat**	10 Mon
11 Thu	11 **Sun**	11 Tue
12 Fri	12 Mon	12 Wed
13 **Sat**	13 Tue	13 Thu
14 **Sun**	14 Wed	14 Fri
15 Mon	15 Thu	15 **Sat**
16 Tue	16 Fri	16 **Sun**
17 Wed	17 **Sat**	17 Mon
18 Thu	18 **Sun**	18 Tue
19 Fri	19 Mon	19 Wed
20 **Sat**	20 Tue	20 Thu
21 **Sun**	21 Wed	21 Fri
22 Mon	22 Thu	22 **Sat**
23 Tue	23 Fri	23 **Sun**
24 Wed	24 **Sat**	24 Mon
25 Thu	25 **Sun**	25 Tue — BANK HOLIDAY
26 Fri	26 Mon	26 Wed — BANK HOLIDAY
27 **Sat**	27 Tue	27 Thu
28 **Sun**	28 Wed	28 Fri
29 Mon	29 Thu	29 **Sat**
30 Tue	30 Fri	30 **Sun**
31 Wed		31 Mon

Acknowledgements

Executive Editor
Nick Rowe
Managing Editor
Emily Davenport

Editor
Marion Paull
Art Editor
Karen Perry

Front Cover Image
Winfried Heinze
Production
Cath Linter

Recipes

Photographer
Food Stylist
Props Stylist
Recipe Testing

Nutritional analysis

Emily Davenport
Sara Lewis

Steve Lee
Sara Lewis
Olivia Wardle
Katy Hackforth
Claire Nadin
Laura Pickering
Gudrun Waskett

Paul McArdle

Special thanks Aune Butt
Chelsea Gray,
Seasonal Berries
Poppy Jones, *Eblex*
Pam Lloyd,
British Asparagus
Graham Meigh
Penny Meigh
Same Sky
Denise
  Spencer-Walker,
Eblex
Hazel Terry
Laura Tomlinson,
BLSA

Published by Eaglemoss Ltd

Electra House, Electra Way, Crewe Business Park, Crewe, Cheshire CW1 6GL

Dairy Diary orders telephone: 0845 0948 128

Queries telephone: 01270 270050

Website: dairydiary.co.uk

Blog: dairydiarychat.co.uk

While every care has been taken in compiling the information in this Diary, the publishers cannot accept responsibility for any errors, inadvertent or not, that may be found or may occur at some time in future owing to changes in legislation or any other reason. © Eaglemoss Ltd 2016

ISBN 978-0-9932105-0-1

PICTURE CREDITS

Front Cover StockFood/Winfried Heinze; 8 Thinkstock/LDProd; 22 Thinkstock/Allou;
24 Shutterstock.com/Alexander Mazurkevich; 25 (tr) Trinity Mirror/Mirrorpix/Alamy,
(bl) Shutterstock.com/Willequet Manuel; 26 bikeriderlondon / Shutterstock.com;
28 Sandra Cunningham / Shutterstock.com; 30 Thinkstock/Kazoka; 32 Eaglemoss/Steve Lee;
34 Bake Club/ Clive Bozzard-Hill; 36 Bake Club/Sian Irvine; 38 GAP Photos/Joanna Kossak;
39 GAP Photos/Elke Borkowski; 40 GAP Photos/Christa Brand; 41 Val Corbett; 42 Thinkstock/
Upyanose; 44 (tl) www.nationalarchives.gov.uk, (bl) Thinkstock/Melanjurga, (tr) R & L Davenport,
(mr) Maureen Rogers, (br) Thinkstock/Ron Chapple Studios; 45 Getty Images/Hulton Collection;
46 Shutterstock.com/Gavin Morrison; 47 (tl) Shutterstock.com/David Muscroft, (tr) Shutterstock.com/
David Fowler, (b) Shutterstock.com/Christopher Elwell; 48 Ray Gibson; 49 Hazel Terry; 50 Thinkstock/
Fuse; 51 Vidados; 52 Project Mapping/Andrew Smithers; 53–159 Eaglemoss/Steve Lee except: 69, 81,
95, 103, 125 simplybeefandlamb.co.uk/Steve Lee; 129, 153, 159 seasonalberries.co.uk/Tony Briscoe;
makemoreofsalad.com 63,117, 127 british-asparagus.co.uk 91, 97; 169–171 Eaglemoss/Steve Lee